PREHISTORIC CREATURES
OF THE
ORDER

A TEMPLAR BOOK

First published in the UK in 2020 by Templar Books,
an imprint of Bonnier Books UK,
The Plaza, 535 King's Road, London, SW10 0SZ
www.templarco.co.uk
www.bonnierbooks.co.uk

Copyright © 2020 by Templar Books

1 3 5 7 9 10 8 6 4 2

ISBN 978-1-78741-344-3

Written by Jules Howard
Illustrated by Kelsey Oseid
Edited by Susie Rae
Designed by Wendy Bartlet
Production Controller Nick Read

Printed in China

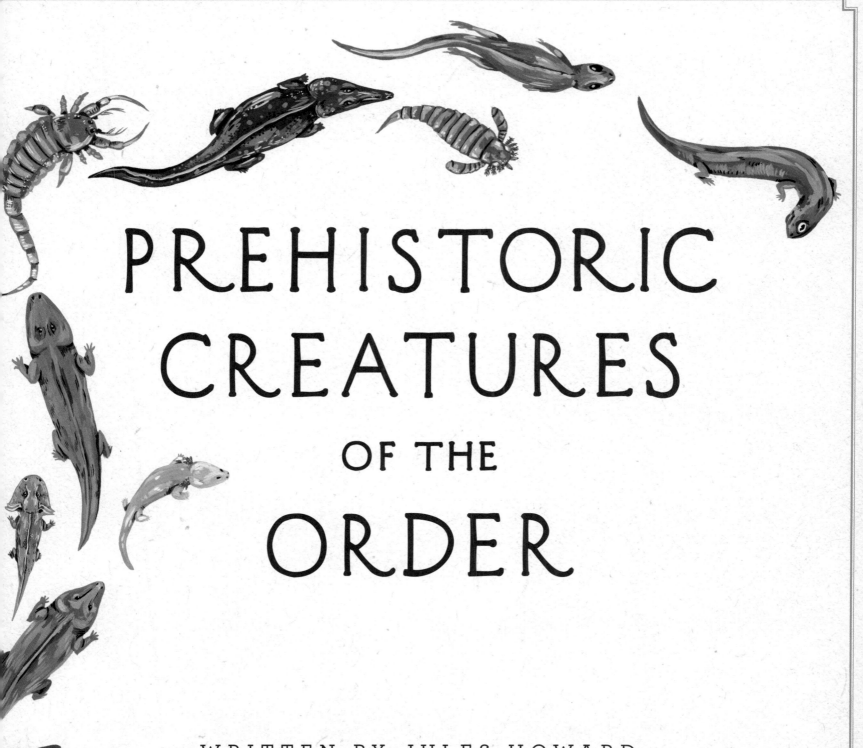

PREHISTORIC CREATURES

OF THE

ORDER

WRITTEN BY JULES HOWARD

ILLUSTRATED BY KELSEY OSEID

templar
books

CONTENTS

PREHISTORIC
CREATURES
OF THE
ORDER

P. 15

P. 18

P. 35

P. 30

P. 27

P. 42

P. 58

P. 63

P. 66

P. 71

P. 23

P. 38

P. 47

P. 55

P. 51

P. 74

INTRODUCTION

Taxonomy is the branch of science that looks at the classification of animals. This book is a celebration of one unit of taxonomy – the order. Every animal is a member of an order, a special type of extended family sharing similar traits. While exploring the prehistoric orders of life, you will truly get to appreciate and understand the incredible, branching family tree of life on Earth, and discover that every animal that has ever existed is merely a beautiful, yet often temporary, variation on a theme.

The fossils beneath our feet tell us a story. It is a story of many millions of creatures battling for food, for space and for survival. It is a story of failure and success that spans continents that have smashed and crashed against one another for a billion years or more. It is a story involving a cast of incredible characters – some predators, some prey; some small, some big; and some, like many dinosaurs, monstrous.

Many of the characters in this book may look strange, but all of them – unlike in fictional stories – are real. The facts of this story have been gathered through many years of hard work by scientists that work around the world carefully preparing and investigating each of the fossils they discover. Like detectives, these scientists use fossils as if they were key pieces of evidence in a crime scene. But theirs is a crime scene like no other. It has taken place over millions of years and involved many millions of creatures. There is a certain chaos to this crime scene. A jumble of information. To make sense of this chaos scientists use a special system to try to classify each animal and plant fossils that they find. To do this, they use taxonomy, a centuries-old scientific method that helps us make sense of the spectacular diversity of life on Earth.

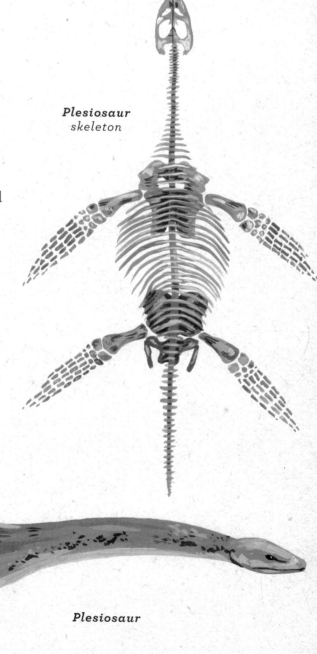

Plesiosaur
skeleton

Plesiosaur

Ornithischian

Ichthyosaur

Carnivoran

Phacopid trilobite

On the pages of this book are arranged illustrations that will show you the various orders of animals that lived in the prehistoric world. Included are two orders of dinosaurs (the saurischians and ornithischians), alongside reptilian cousins that ruled the sky (the pterosaurs) and reptile orders that ruled the seas (the plesiosaurs and the ichthyosaurs). Then there are the creatures that came to replace them millions of years later: the predatory birds that took the top spot in South America (the cariamiformes), the mammalian meat-eaters (carnivorans), the Australian megafauna (the diprotodontians), the trunked (proboscideans) and the titanic (the pilosans). In the early stages of this book, there are the orders that stirred in the seas and swamps long before there were dinosaurs. From the simple (the arthrodires and the eurypterids) to the complex (the phacopid trilobites). From the mini (the microsaurs) to the massive (the temnospondyls).

As you flick through the pages of this book, remember that these animals had lives and remember that they lived and breathed and fought and struggled as animals do today. On each page the animals share history. They share bones. They share ancestors. They share a family grouping – this is their order.

Caecilian

Pterosaur

Saurischian

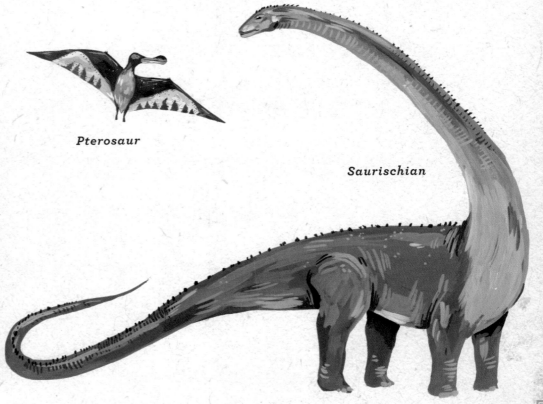

ANIMAL CLASSIFICATION

The more one investigates the life forms of Planet Earth, the more one notices that each organism can be divided into neat categories. The names of these categories were first put forward by a Swedish naturalist living in the 1700s called Carl Linnaeus. Linnaeus devised a system known as taxonomy, which was designed to organise nature into groups according to their characteristics. It is a system scientists still use today to understand where creatures belong in the family tree of life on Earth.

WHAT IS AN ORDER?

Within each group of animals or plants are smaller groups that can then be categorised into smaller groups still. This is the essence of taxonomy. The sabre-toothed cat, for instance, can be grouped together with the mammoth, because females of both species gave birth to live babies that they fed with milk. This is a characteristic of the group or 'class' Mammalia. However, look more closely at these animals and you will notice that the sabre-toothed cat was clearly different from the mammoth. Like modern-day lions, tigers and wolves, sabre-toothed cats possessed large, sharp-edged molars and giant canine teeth. Together, these carnivorous mammals can be grouped together in a category of their own – this category is called an order. The sabre-toothed cat is a mammal of an order named Carnivora. Mammoths, with their distinctive muscular trunk and tusks, are a different kind of mammal. They belong with elephants in a different order, Proboscidea.

Mammoth

Sabre-toothed cat

KINGDOM

On the broadest level, organisms can be divided into groups by looking at the types of cells they are made of. Animals, plants and fungi are each made of unique types of cells and therefore make up three of the six known kingdoms of life on Earth.

PHYLUM

The organisms in a phylum share the same broader characteristics. For instance, animals with a nerve cord running along the middle of the body (including back boned creatures) are united in the phylum Chordata.

CLASS

This can be divided into more manageable chunks by looking at broad body characteristics, such as the way that they reproduce. In animals of the phylum Chordata, the classes of animals include mammals, amphibians and reptiles.

ORDER

Orders are variations on a theme within a class. Of amphibians, for instance, frogs and toads are grouped together as tailless amphibians (order Anura) and salamanders and newts are considered tailed amphibians (order Urodela).

FAMILY

Within orders, there are distinct families made of creatures that start to look quite alike. Chickens, for instance, are grouped in a family of birds called the Phasianidae that all share pheasant-like features.

GENUS

Animals within a genus share more recent ancestors and therefore look closer still. Lions and tigers, for instance, are both members of the genus Panthera, which also includes jaguars and leopards.

SPECIES

Most scientists define a species as a group of organisms that can interbreed and produce healthy offspring that can then grow up to produce their own offspring. There may be as many as two million different animal species on Earth.

ANIMAL CLASSIFICATION
of the terror bird

KINGDOM	ANIMALIA
PHYLUM	CHORDATA
CLASS	AVES
ORDER	CARIAMIFORMES
FAMILY	PHORUSRHACIDAE
GENUS	PHORUSRHACOS
SPECIES	PHORUSRHACOS LONGISSIMUS

DISCOVERING
PREHISTORIC ORDERS

Scientists like to examine the fossils (the remains of a plant or an animal preserved in rock) of prehistoric creatures. They look for clues in the structure of these ancient body parts to help them discover which animal families and orders were alive at the time and how they fitted together throughout history. By doing this, they continue the work that scientists began over 200 years ago.

Every fact in this book has been verified by a scientist or group of scientists who discovered it from a fossil. The discovery of fossils is how we know so much about prehistoric creatures.

Many fossils are of animal bones and teeth. This is because the bones and teeth are the parts that are the hardest, so other animals wouldn't eat them and bacteria struggle to decompose them. Once buried in mud and sand and other sediments, these bones and teeth are replaced over many years by minerals and become fossils.

Fossils have been found on all of the continents on Earth, including under the ice of Antarctica. Wherever you are reading this, there might be fossils underneath you right now, deep under the ground in a layer of sedimentary rock. Humans will never get to see most of these hidden fossils that are frozen in time underground, but sometimes fossils become exposed, on eroding cliff faces or on the banks of streams and rivers. Many of the most spectacular fossils were found by people noticing a strange shape sticking out from a rock and investigating further.

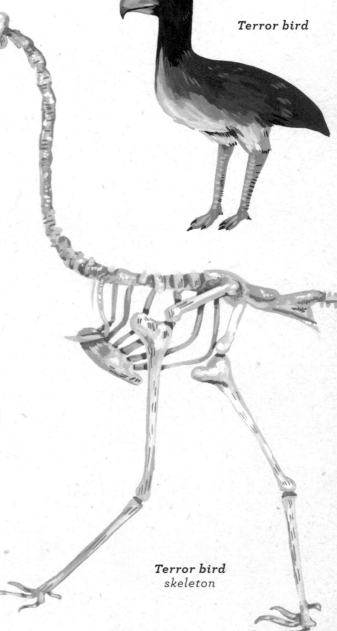

Terror bird

Terror bird
skeleton

READING THE LAYERS IN THE ROCKS

CENOZOIC
66 MILLION YEARS AGO

QUATERNARY

NEOGENE

PALEOGENE

MESOZOIC
252–66 MILLION YEARS AGO

CRETACEOUS

JURASSIC

TRIASSIC

PALAEOZOIC
541–252 MILLION YEARS AGO

PERMIAN

CARBONIFEROUS

DEVONIAN

SILURIAN

ORDOVICIAN

CAMBRIAN

Scientists have found that a pattern emerges in the layers of the Earth. Often the deeper we dig, the further back in time the fossils we discover. This means that a cliff face of exposed rock has the newest rocks at the top and the oldest rocks at the bottom. Rock scientists, called geologists, study these layers and map them out in order of time, ensuring each layer is dated correctly.

Fossil scientists, called palaeontologists, use these findings to order the history of life on Earth and to understand how animals have changed over many millions of years. They are also able to see how animals were affected by remarkable mass extinction events, like the one that killed off most of the dinosaurs, and if they recovered.

Layers of earth are dated into three main categories. Fossils from the Palaeozoic era tell us about the world before dinosaurs, when amphibians and early reptiles lived, and after that, the age of the armoured fish and early sharks. Mesozoic fossils tell us about the world during the rise and fall of large reptiles, particularly the dinosaurs. Cenozoic fossils relate to the period after the dinosaurs, when it was the turn of the mammals to rise in power.

These three great eras can be divided into smaller chunks, of course. The Mesozoic, for instance, is split into three smaller sections, called periods. First, the Triassic period (from 252 million to 201 million years ago); then the Jurassic period (from 201 million to 145 million years ago); and then, finally, the Cretaceous period (from 145 million years to 66 million years ago).

PREHISTORIC
CREATURES
OF THE
ORDER

PHACOPIDA

LATE CAMBRIAN TO LATE DEVONIAN

The Phacopida was an order of trilobite, a highly adaptable and specialised group of invertebrates that were incredibly successful during the Palaeozoic period. Though they lived in water, these were the insects of their day. These specialised creatures had up to 15,000 eyes and each eye contained rows of light-sensitive lenses that allowed them to see in nearly all directions. In the Devonian oceans, where predators, such as sharks, were evolving, these eyes gave the phacopids a fighting chance of survival, and saw them develop into one of the world's most successful trilobite groups.

1. CHEIRURUS INGRICUS

When *Cheirurus ingricus* rolled up its body, its long head spines hooked forwards, perhaps impaling potential predators. It first evolved in the late stages of the Cambrian period, when the earliest ocean creatures (including jawless fish) were just developing.

Cheirurus ingricus

2. COLTRANEIA OUFATENENSIS

As fish began to develop jaws and teeth, trilobites' senses evolved so they could see them coming. With its huge, bug-like eyes, *Coltraneia oufatenensis* was one such trilobite. Each layer within its eyes had 14 lenses, giving it a panoramic view of the world.

3. PHACOPS RANA

Many trilobites could roll into a ball for protection, but *Phacops rana* mastered it better than any other. This defence mechanism may have been one of the reasons for its near-global success.

4. DALMANITES LIMULURUS

The teardrop shaped *Dalmanites limulurus* is thought to have rested in soft sand, to hide from predators or ambush small prey. The purpose of its tail-spike is unknown, but it may have helped to reduce drag as it moved.

5. GYROMETOPUS LINEATUS

When rolled up into a ball, *Gyrometopus lineatus* was about the size of a pea, and likely went unnoticed by many predators. Some of its features suggest it had close links to the first Phacopida trilobites from the late Cambrian period. Due to this, some palaeontologists see it as a 'living fossil' of its time.

Gyrometopus lineatus

6. MOROCCONITES MALLADOIDES

Morocconites malladoides' mysterious beak-like horn sticking out the front of its head may have been used for combat with other individuals, or may have helped it shake up sand on the sea floor, exposing food underneath.

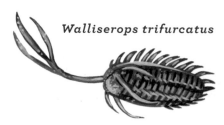

Walliserops trifurcatus

7. WALLISEROPS TRIFURCATUS

Scientists have debated for years about why this trilobite had a fork on its head. It may have used it to show off how healthy it was, or to joust with other males to impress members of the opposite sex.

8. PSYCHOPYGE ELEGANS

Psychopyge elegans had a mysterious sword-like protrusion upon its head. This strange adaptation may have been used to sift through sand, feeling for prey. However, some scientists argue that this 'sword' may have been used in fights between male rivals eager to gain the approval of females.

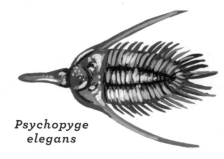

Psychopyge elegans

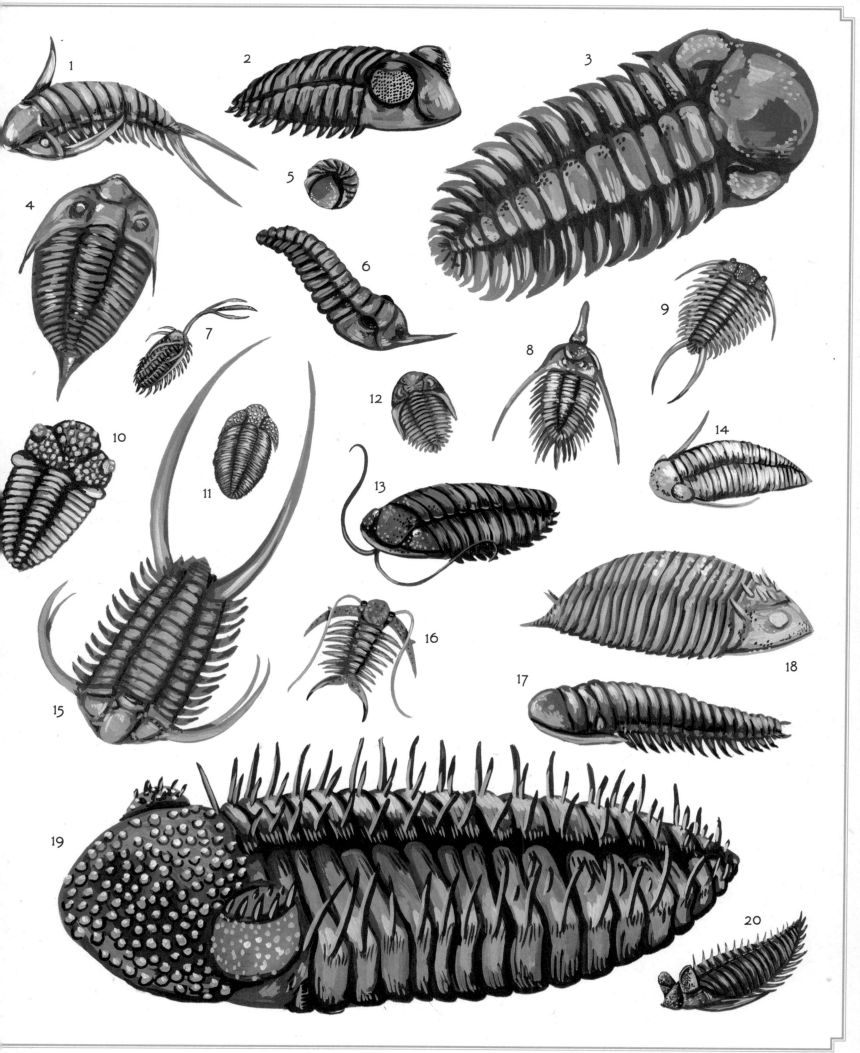

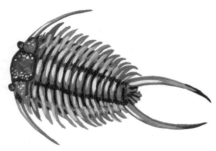

Ceraurus pleurexanthemus

9. CERAURUS PLEUREXANTHEMUS

Impressive spines curved from the body of this small trilobite. These may have helped protect it from predators, though some scientists think they might have worked like snowshoes, keeping *Ceraurus pleurexanthemus* from sinking into silt and mud.

10. BALIZOMA VARIOLARIS

This is one of the so-called 'strawberry-headed trilobites' known from fossil pits in the West Midlands, England. Its head was covered with small lumps. They may have helped *Balizoma variolaris* to camouflage in the sand, or made them harder for octopus-like predators to get a good grip on.

11. AEGROTOCATELLUS JAGGERI

Named after rock star Mick Jagger, *Aegrotocatellus jaggeri* belongs to a special family of tiny trilobites that dominated the world's seas 450 million years ago. Some were only 2.5 cm (1 in) long – little more than the size of a paperclip.

Aegrotocatellus jaggeri

12. GREENOPS BARBERI

Like other trilobites of this order, the eyes of *Greenops barberi* were large and would have been sensitive to the tell-tale movements of incoming predators. With short, sharp spines that ran across its tail area, *Greenops barberi* was not to be angered.

13. CALYMENE BLUMENBACHII

Calymene blumenbachii pursued its prey through early coral reefs. In the 1700s, miners in Dudley, a town in central England, discovered so many of these fossils they nicknamed them 'Dudley bugs' – a name still used locally to describe trilobites.

14. CHASMOPS ODINI

The eyes of *Chasmops odini* could do more than just spot approaching predators. Their large size and location on the head suggest that this trilobite also used its keen vision to locate and chase after moving prey.

Chasmops odini

15. PARACERAURUS EXSUL

This large trilobite's spines may have helped to stop it from sinking into the muddy sea floor and getting stuck. *Paraceraurus exsul* lived at a time when sea creatures were mostly squid-like and jawed fish were only just beginning to evolve.

16. DEIPHON FORBESI

Deiphon forbesi was probably a free-swimming trilobite. Its rounded head region may have been filled with oils to help it float in the water. Long spines along the body may have put off early jawed fish, including sharks.

Deiphon forbesi

Crotalocephalina gibbus

17. CROTALOCEPHALINA GIBBUS

When fossils of this centipede-like trilobite were first discovered, the head regions reminded scientists of a rattlesnake. Measuring about 7.5 cm (3 in), it likely snaked across the sea floor, searching for food.

18. HOMALONOTUS ARMATUS

Homalonotus armatus and its close cousins lived for almost 80 million years, with fossils discovered in Europe, North and South America, and even New Zealand. This successful and adaptable trilobite was likely a fast-moving sea floor carnivore.

Homalonotus armatus

19. DROTOPS ARMATUS

This large trilobite was almost the size of a dinner plate. It was covered in sharp spines that may have protected it from predators. The spines were found above its impressive eyes, which provided it with wraparound vision.

20. ERBENOCHILE ERBENI

The eyes of *Erbenochile erbeni* were unique. Containing over 500 lenses, they were stacked upon the head and worked almost like a periscope. The eyes even had little eyeshades, suggesting it was a daytime hunter in shallow seas.

Erbenochile erbeni

FIGURE 1. PHACOPID EYES

The eyes of the phacopids were incredibly sensitive. Each eye consisted of lots of rows of individual lenses that had a completely see through crystal structure. These lenses focused light on to special light-processing cells which fed messages to the brain about objects moving across their field of view. Creatures in this order had as many as 700 individual lenses in each eye and they pointed in different directions, allowing for 360-degree vision in many species. As bigger and more dangerous predators (such as jawed fish, including sharks) began to evolve, this heightened vision helped phacopids avoid becoming prey.

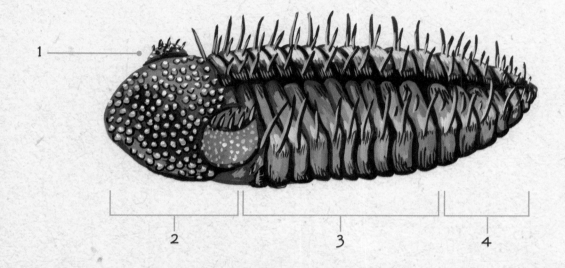

1. *Compound eyes*
2. *Cephalon (head)*
3. *Thorax (throat)*
4. *Pydgium (rear)*

FIGURE 2. ORDER ISOPODA

Trilobites shared the oceans with another early order of marine creatures that also had a hard exoskeleton. These were known as isopods (order Isopoda). Three hundred million years ago, these slow-moving creatures lived a benthic existence, crawling or burrowing in soft sediments on the sea floor, looking for decomposing plants or animals to feed upon. Some isopods evolved to live in the deep sea (where they remain today) and others evolved to become shore-dwellers called sea slaters. One small part of this order, known as woodlice, invaded the land and have become incredibly important parts of modern ecosystems.

Giant isopods

ARTHRODIRA

EARLY TO LATE DEVONIAN

The arthrodires were an order of fish that were known for their armoured heads, covered in tough, bony plates and for their toothless, beak-like jaws. They filled the world's oceans, occupying many roles, before a mysterious extinction wiped them out 360 million years ago. Among their ranks were piranha-like scavengers and monstrous predators including *Dunkleosteus terrelli* (p. 20) – a powerful carnivore, the likes of which the world had never seen before. For a long time, scientists considered arthrodires to be simple fish that were pushed aside by modern-day sharks and other fish species. However, a new wave of fossil discoveries showed that they were anything but.

1. TITANICHTHYS CLARKIA

Though it rivalled *Dunkleosteus terrelli* in size, *Titanichthys clarkia* lacked powerful, armour-piercing jaws. Instead, it may have been a filter feeder that opened its vast mouth to scoop up and sieve out small marine invertebrates from the water.

2. RHACHIOSTEUS PTERYGIATUS

With a skull the size of a small bean, *Rhachiosteus pterygiatus* was so tiny that some scientists wonder if its fossil could have been mistaken for a baby of another species. What advantage it got from its size is still a mystery.

3. YIMINASPIS SHENME

Yiminaspis shenme has only recently become known to scientists who, in 2008, found fossils of its skull and body armour. Its flattened head suggests it was a bottom-dweller, using its beak to pull apart food on the sea floor.

Yiminaspis shenme

Antarctaspis mcmurdoensis

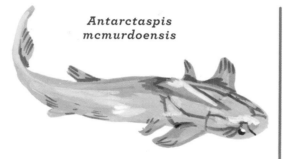

4. ANTARCTASPIS MCMURDOENSIS

Fossils like *Antarctaspis mcmurdoensis* come from an incredible fossil bed called the Gogo Formation in Australia's western regions. Each year, more and more new arthrodires are discovered from this important site.

5. DINICHTHYS HERZERI

Early sharks lived in the shadow of a giant arthrodire known as *Dinichthys herzeri*. Though only a few fossils of its skull and body armour have ever been found, it is likely to have been approximately the same size as *Dunkleosteus terrelli*.

6. COCCOSTEUS CUSPIDATUS

Coccosteus cuspidatus was the piranha of its age. It had self-sharpening, beak-like jaws that could bite through fish armour, and a bony joint at the back of its skull that allowed its jaws to open wider than many other predators.

7. DRACONICHTHYS ELEGANS

Though little more than 60 cm (23 in) long, *Draconichthys elegans* was designed to be a predator. It had armour-plated jaws armed with sharp points, almost like shark teeth. These 'gnathal plates' were used to hold its prey in place before swallowing.

8. SELENOSTEUS BREVIS

This shark-like swimmer is known for its giant eyes, which may have helped it spot prey or predators like *Dinichthys* and *Dunkleosteus*. Known from only a few fossils, scientists are keen to learn more about this creature.

Selenosteus brevis

9. ERROLOSTEUS GOODRADIGBEENSIS

Errolosteus goodradigbeensis possessed a small head and a pair of extremely large eyes. This mysterious creature is known from a handful of fossils of skull and armour plating fragments discovered in New South Wales, Australia.

Dunkleosteus terrelli

10. DUNKLEOSTEUS TERRELLI

Before there were killer sharks and monstrous dinosaurs, this ancient apex predator dwarfed nearly all other creatures on Earth. It was 6 m (19 ft) long and its sharp jaws could snap shut with such force that it could slice most modern predators in half with a single bite.

11. AUSTROPHYLLOLEPIS RITCHIEI

Austrophyllolepis ritchiei was an arthrodire known for the giant armoured plates on its back. These shell-like plates gave it a flat shape similar to a stingray. Using its fins, it may have shifted the sand on the sea floor, exposing potential prey.

Rolfosteus canningensis

12. ROLFOSTEUS CANNINGENSIS

This mackerel-sized arthrodire was like a miniature shark, with a pointed snout that reduced drag as it swam. As with modern-day sharks, it probably had a keen sense of smell, helping it locate prey.

13. HOLDENIUS HOLDENI

Holdenius holdeni is believed to have had eyes bigger than its stomach. One famous fossil shows one with a shark in its jaws, which it had just captured. Unfortunately, the shark's spiny dorsal fin appeared to have pierced the arthrodire's brain as it swallowed it, instantly killing it.

14. AFRICANASPIS EDMOUNTAINI

Africanaspis edmountaini was discovered by South African fossil-hunters in 2017. It had an enormous dorsal fin for its size and an unarmoured muscular tail, which it used to propel itself forward. Its long pectoral fins probably stopped its head being dragged downwards as it swam.

Africanaspis edmountaini

15. ALEOSTEUS EGANENSIS

Though *Aleosteus eganensis'* armour offered it protection from predators, the heavy, bony plates weighed it down and made it a poor swimmer. Instead, it probably lived on the sea floor.

16. ARENIPISCIS WESTOLLI

Arenipiscis westolli is known for a strange grainy covering on its armoured plating. Scientists have not yet discovered the purpose of this unusual texture, but one idea is that it may have helped *Arenipiscis westolli* blend in amongst its surroundings.

Arenipiscis westolli

17. ACTINOLEPIS SPINOSA

This tiny arthrodire was easy to miss. At just 10 cm (4 in) long, *Actinolepis spinosa* could fit comfortably in a human palm. Part of a successful family of arthrodires called the Actinolepidae, they thrived in the world's oceans during the Devonian period.

Actinolepis spinosa

18. GORGONICHTHYS CLARKI

Gorgonichthys clarki rivaled *Dunkleosteus terrelli* for the title of the longest arthrodire. Some specimens suggest it was 6 m (19 ft) long, almost the size of the largest killer whales today. Though heavily armoured, it was a lighter build than many arthrodire predators.

19. TIARASPIS STRUDENSIS

Like many modern-day fish, *Tiaraspis strudensis* may have migrated to have its babies. Fossils of juveniles suggest that its young stayed near river deltas, feasting on nutrient-rich waters before moving into the open sea when they reached adulthood.

Tiaraspis strudensis

20. WUTTAGOONASPIS FLETCHERI

The box-like skull of *Wuttagoonaspis fletcheri* likely held powerful muscles to open and close its jaws. It had a pair of plate-like pieces of armour, about the size of a human palm, on the uppermost side of its body.

FIGURE 1. ARTHRODIRE SKULL

Arthrodires had a moveable joint between their head shield and body armour. By lifting their head shield upwards whilst opening their jaws, they could open their mouths extremely wide and snap them shut with impressive force. All arthrodires lacked teeth. Instead, they relied upon beak-like jaws with sharp edges that could bite through body armour and, occasionally, the bone of other arthrodires. Arthrodires are also known for having bones around their eyeballs. This ring of bone protected their eyeballs from damage and may have also kept their eyeballs from shrinking under the intense water pressure in the deep ocean.

1. *Nuchal gap*
2. *Cranio-thoracic joint*
3. *Orbit*
4. *Bladed dentition*
5. *Inferognathal (lower jaw)*
6. *Pharynx*
7. *Thoracic shield*
8. *Keel*

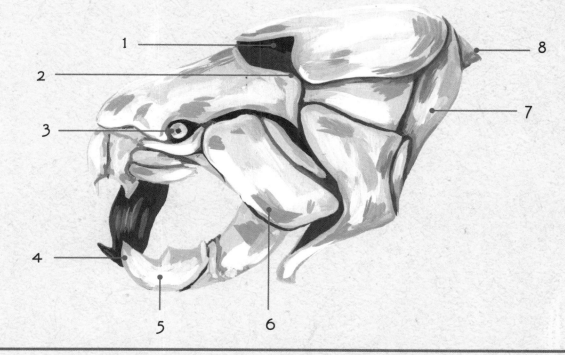

FIGURE 2: CHIMAERIFORMES

At about the same time that the arthrodires were starting to dominate marine ecosystems, a secretive order of jawed fish was emerging from the depths. They were the chimaeras (order Chimaeriformes). These ghostly fish looked a bit like small sharks but, instead of sharp teeth, they had bony plates for grinding food. Today, there are 50 living Chimaeriform species that are known, and there are likely several others that scientists have not yet discovered.

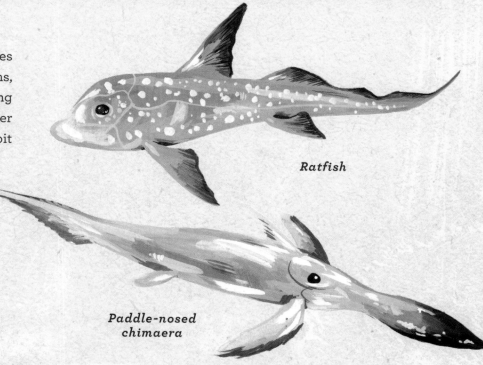

Ratfish

Paddle-nosed chimaera

EURYPTERIDS

EARLY ORDOVICIAN TO LATE PERMIAN

Eurypterids had scorpion-like bodies and are loosely known as 'sea scorpions'. They include one of the biggest invertebrate predators that ever lived – *Jaekelopterus* – a 3-m-(10-ft)-long apex hunter. However, many species of this order were far smaller and often measured just 20 cm (8 in). Eurypterids were unpredictable in their behaviours and habitats. For more than 200 million years, these creatures came to dominate reefs, swamps and shallow seas around the world. Scientists are still trying to find out exactly why this branch of the invertebrate family tree went extinct 252 million years ago.

Hughmilleria socialis

1. HUGHMILLERIA SOCIALIS

This palm-sized euryptid dominated freshwater communities, 400 million years ago. It is likely to have bullied horseshoe crabs and shrimp-like crustaceans out of the way as it searched for food in the mud and sand.

2. PTERYGOTUS ANGLICUS

Pterygotus anglicus was a fast and agile marine predator. At 1.6 m (5.3 ft) from head to tail, it was about three times longer than a modern-day lobster. It is thought to have used its large claws to strip prey into bite-sized chunks.

3. ACUTIRAMUS CUMMINGSI

Acutiramus cummingsi differed from other monstrous euryptids. Its eyes were less sensitive and its claws were used for shearing rather than crushing. Scientists suspect it was an ambush predator that hunted under the darkness of night.

4. DREPANOPTERUS PENTLANDICUS

Drepanopterus pentlandicus may have shared its habitat with some of the earliest fish that began to explore land around 400 million years ago. Scientists consider it to be an early ancestor of *Hibbertopterus,* the giant swamp-dweller.

5. RHENOPTERUS DIENSTI

With its small, bulb-like head and beady eyes, *Rhenopterus diensti* is unlikely to have been an active predator. Instead, this euryptid probably crawled along the sea floor, attracted to the smell of rotting creatures.

Rhenopterus diensti

6. CTENOPTERUS CESTROTUS

With a thin body and long, spiny legs, *Ctenopterus cestrotus* was almost spider-like. These long legs may have helped it to move quickly across the sea floor, helping it to be the first to arrive at a fresh corpse.

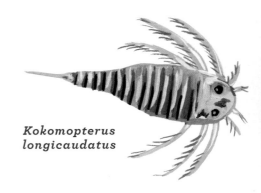

Kokomopterus longicaudatus

7. KOKOMOPTERUS LONGICAUDATUS

Kokomopterus longicaudatus is named after Kokomo, the US city in which fossils of this euryptid were first found. This euryptid crawled across the sea floor, much like crabs and lobsters do today.

8. HALLIPTERUS EXCELSIOR

Hallipterus excelsior's tiny eyes sat on the top of its head, giving it a scorpion-like appearance. It is likely to have buried itself in sand, leaving only its eyes sticking out, which protected it from predatory jawed fish.

9. MEGARACHNE SERVINEI

When fossils of *Megarachne servinei* were first discovered, scientists thought it was a giant spider. Its small compound eyes and long, blade-like appendages suggest it was, like many freshwater euryptids, a sweep-feeder.

10. EURYPTERUS REMIPES

Thousands of *Eurypterus remipes* fossils have been dug up over the past 200 years, making it something of a Palaeozoic celebrity. It swam like a giant water beetle, rowing a pair of oar-like legs whilst searching for prey.

11. MEGALOGRAPTUS WELCHI

This impressive, 1.2-m-(3.9-ft)-long creature had long spines in the middle of its blades. Scientists are still debating what these were used for. Although they look dangerous, they may have been used to sift through sand, feeling for prey underneath.

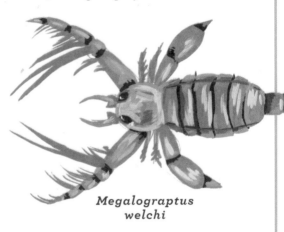

Megalograptus welchi

12. HIBBERTOPTERUS SCOULERI

This curious euryptid was a sweep-feeder. It used its claw-like blades to rake through mud, searching for small invertebrates to eat. *Hibbertopterus scouleri* was a giant, with a head too big to fit through a door frame.

13. JAEKELOPTERUS RHENANIAE

With claw-tipped blades almost as long as human arms and a body twice as long as a sofa, *Jaekelopterus rhenaniae* was one of the largest and most fearsome invertebrates ever. This was one of the world's first apex predators.

14. DUNSOPTERUS STEVENSONI

Dunsopterus stevensoni is perhaps the most mysterious euryptid, known only from a few chunks of fossilised armour and pieces of skin. Scientists think it was around 1 m (3 ft) in length and might have resembled other sweep-feeding freshwater euryptids.

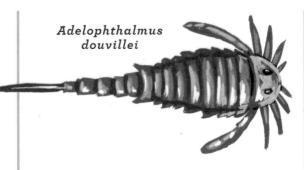

Adelophthalmus douvillei

15. ADELOPHTHALMUS DOUVILLEI

Small enough to perch on a human finger, *Adelophthalmus douvillei* was one of the tiniest euryptids. It swam with powerful legs and likely hunted on the sea bed, sifting its blades through the mud in search of prey.

16. MIXOPTERIS KIAERI

The dagger-like spines on the blades of *Mixopteris kiaeri* were among the deadliest of euryptid weapons. They grasped and held prey steady while the tail lashed forwards like a scorpion to deliver the killing blow.

Mixopteris kiaeri

17. CARCINOSOMA NEWLINE

Scientists are not yet sure why *Carcinosoma newline* was covered in tiny bumps, called tubercles. These may have helped it to camouflage from the jawed fish who were becoming the most fearsome predators of the sea.

18. BRACHYOPTERUS STUBBLEFIELDI

This cat-sized euryptid lacked legs for swimming, and preferred walking upon the sea floor searching for creatures to scavenge. *Brachyopterus stubblefieldi* was an early aquatic pioneer. Alongside its relatives, it colonised the world and cemented the reputation of euryptids as a force to be reckoned with.

19. CAMPYLOCEPHALUS PERMIANUS

While early reptiles and amphibians invaded the land, this euryptid sifted through swamp mud, searching for invertebrates to eat. *Campylocephalus permianus* was likely killed in an extinction event 252 million years ago.

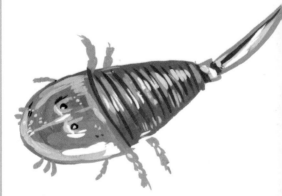

Campylocephalus permianus

20. PENTECOPTERUS DECORAHENSIS

Pentecopterus decorahensis was a monstrous scavenger that lived alongside early fish, 465 million years ago. It had an estimated length similar to an adult human, and may have lived in shallow, swamp-like waters.

FIGURE 1. EURYPTERID APPENDAGES

All eurypterids had a highly decorated pair of spines and needles (and in some cases, claws) at the front of their body. They also had four pairs of legs used for moving along sandy and muddy surfaces. In some species, a sixth pair of legs was adapted into paddle-like structures that could be rowed like oars through the water. This group became the fastest and most predatory eurypterids. All species have an obvious spine, called the telson, which is believed to have been highly mobile, but scientists don't yet know if eurypterids had venomous tail stings.

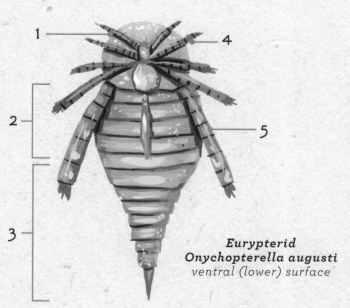

Eurypterid
Onychopterella augusti
ventral (lower) surface

1. *Walking legs*
2. *Mesosoma*
3. *Metasoma*
4. *Walking legs*
5. *Swimming paddle*

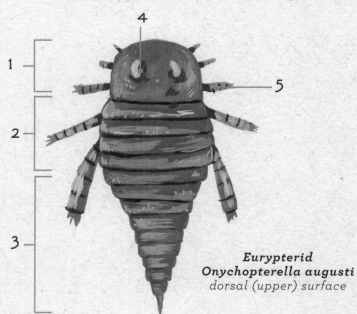

Eurypterid
Onychopterella augusti
dorsal (upper) surface

1. *Prosoma*
2. *Mesosoma*
3. *Metasoma*
4. *Compound eye*
5. *Walking legs*

FIGURE 2. SCORPION

While the eurypterids were colonising the world's seas and freshwaters, a closely related order was making the land its own. These were the scorpions (order Scorpiones). Scorpions possess a modified pair of front legs (with claws) and a long, pointed tail which can be used to inject venom into prey. Today, scorpions have become a highly successful group in the arachnid family tree and around 1,750 species are known from all over the world. The only land mass they haven't yet conquered is Antarctica. The first scorpions may have lived 430 million years ago, but this is an animal order still thriving today.

Emperor scorpion

TEMNOSPONDYLI

EARLY CARBONIFEROUS TO EARLY CRETACEOUS

These highly adaptable amphibians occupied every continent on Earth and flourished in numerous habitats, including coastal waters, beaches, swamps and forests. Though many temnospondyls were relatively small, some may have reached lengths of more than 11 m (36 ft). All species had a complicated back bones (vertebrae), which were split up into a number of separate parts. Because fossils show that many early reptiles and amphibians both had these unusual back bones, some scientists have argued that this order of animals might need to be reassessed.

Rhinesuchus whaitsi

1. RHINESUCHUS WHAITSI

Rhinesuchus whaitsi had small, bulbous eyes that poked out from the top of its head. This, along with its tooth-filled jaws, suggested that it lay on the bottom of swamps and lakes, hunting prey from below. It is thought to have died out during an extinction event called the Great Dying, 252 million years ago.

2. PRIONOSUCHUS PLUMMERI

At 9 m (29 ft) long, *Prionosuchus plummeri* was one of the largest and most ferocious of the temnospondyls. This aquatic predator would easily dwarf a saltwater crocodile. Like many ambush predators, it had a very long, thin snout.

3. COCHLEOSAURUS BOHEMICUS

The so-called 'spoon lizard' was named for the spoon-shaped lumps on its skull. This was one of the first crocodile-like temnospondyls. About the size of a chameleon, it may have hunted by ambushing prey from a short range.

4. BROOMISTEGA PUTTERILLI

One famous fossil shows a *Broomistega putterilli* skeleton preserved alongside an early burrowing mammal-like reptile. This suggests that *Broomistega putterilli* was a burrow-stealer that took up home in other animals' burrows.

Broomistega putterilli

5. SCLEROCEPHALUS HAEUSERI

So common was this species that many fossil beds are still packed with their teeth and skeletons today. *Sclerocephalus haeurseri* reached a body length of about 1.5 m (5 ft) and fossils of its gut contents tell us that this early predator fed upon fish and other smaller temnospondyls.

6. CYCLOTOSAURUS ROBUSTUS

Cyclotosaurus robustus was a monstrous temnospondyl that faced extinction at about the same time as the reign of dinosaurs began. It measured more than 4 m (13 ft) and may have hunted both on land and in the water.

Doleserpeton annectens

7. DOLESERPETON ANNECTENS

Studying *Doleserpeton annectens* helps scientists to understand how modern-day amphibians might have evolved. This species had four sprawling legs that dragged its body forwards, allowing it to move on land. It also had four fingers on the fore legs and five on the back, just like amphibians today.

8. TAMBACHIA TROGALLAS

This relatively small temnospondyl had large eyes that may have helped it hunt at night. *Tambachia trogallas* also had a special organ that helped it get rid of excess body salts, called a salt gland. The species name comes from the Greek word for 'sausage', because fossils have been found in a part of Germany famous for its sausages!

Tambachia trogallas

Trimerorhachis insignis

9. TRIMERORHACHIS NSIGNIS

Trimerorhachis insignis had a triangle-shaped head with upward-pointing eyes at the front of the skull, suggesting it was an aquatic predator of fish and amphibians. Some fossils of *Trimerorhachis insignis* suggest that they carried their young in their mouths.

10. EDOPS CRAIGI

With large jaws and a long snout, *Edops craigi* lived up to its name, which means 'glutton face'. Growing to 2 m (7 ft) in length, it was one of the largest land animals of its age. *Edops craigi* lived in what is now the USA, though fossils found in Scotland suggest it could have thrived across large areas of the world.

11. PELTOBATRACHUS PUSTULATUS

Peltobatrachus pustulatus was an armadillo-like temnospondyl that was unlikely to have been able to roll up into a ball, but it did have a layer of armour plating along its body and tail that offered protection from predators.

Peltobatrachus pustulatus

12. MELOSAURUS PLATYRHINUS

In a world before dinosaurs, *Melosaurus platyrhinus* was an apex predator of wetlands, including lakes, rivers and swamps. It fed upon fish and early amphibians, some of which were predators themselves. Up to 3 m (10 ft) in length, it was close to the size of a Nile crocodile.

13. CACOPS ASPIDEPHORUS

Cacops aspidephorus was one of the most terrifying predators of its age. Not only did it have teeth adapted for grasping and pinning down its prey, but it was also one of the first land predators to be able to hear.

14. ACANTHOSTOMATOPS VORAX

Scientists still disagree about what the strange bony points on the sides of the skull of *Acanthostomatops vorax* were for. One theory is that their skulls housed special glands that produced a sticky substance to help their tongues grab escaping prey.

Acanthostomatops vorax

15. MASTODONSAURUS GIGANTEUS

At 6 m (20 ft) long, *Mastodonsaurus giganteus* may have been the largest amphibian that ever lived. It ruled in an age in which the dinosaurs were beginning their rise to power. As well as hunting fish, *Mastodonsaurus giganteus* may have even hunted some small dinosaurs.

16. BRANCHIOSAURUS GRACILIS

If it had lived today, this aquatic temnospondyl would have fit comfortably on a human hand. It's name means 'gill lizard' after the external gills that draped down from the side of its head.

Branchiosaurus gracilis

Cheliderpeton vrayni

17. CHELIDERPETON VRAYNI

Cheliderpeton vrayni was one of the temnospondyls that became adapted for hunting in water and on land, similar to modern-day crocodiles. This family of temnospondyls all had wide heads with big nostrils, probably used for sniffing out prey. *Cheliderpeton vrayni* was about 60 cm (24 in) in length.

18. KONZHUKOVIA VETUSTA

Like other fish-eating temnospondyls, *Konzhukovia vetusta* had an oval head and sharp teeth adapted to catch fish. In 2016, fossils of a close relation were found in Brazil, suggesting that they were widespread hunters during the Permian period.

Archegosaurus decheni

19. ARCHEGOSAURUS DECHENI

This aquatic predator is known from 90 partial skeletons found in Germany. Some of these fossils hint at the digestion and style of breathing of *Archegosaurus decheni*, telling scientists that it had a more fish-like metabolism than modern amphibians.

20. DENDRERPETON ACADIANUM

This species of 1-m-(3-ft)-long temnospondyl may have hidden in forests. Fossils show them squashed within the hollows of early trees. Like many modern amphibians, it may have slept during cold spells.

FIGURE 1. TEMNOSPONDYL METAMORPHOSIS

Many species of this order were first discovered from the fossils of adults and their tadpole-like larvae. These fossils show that temnospondyls had a series of special bones onto which furry gills were attached on the outside of their body. Unlike amphibians today, the larvae of temnospondyls were likely to have been covered in scales. During metamorphosis, the bones in their skull became much thicker and stronger, to prepare the larva for its adult life stage which was often on land.

Larva

Juvenile

Adult

FIGURE 2. ORDER URODELA

Today, the order Urodela gives us some idea of how temnospondyls may have acted and looked in real life. This order of tailed amphibians is best known for salamanders, newts and the almost legless (and almost completely aquatic) sirens.

All urodeles reach adulthood via a larval stage where they live in water and possesses the same frilly-looking external gills as temnospondyls. Some species (such as *Ambystoma mexicanum*) retain their external gills into adulthood, much like we imagine some temnospondyls to have done.

Juvenile salamander

Adult salamander

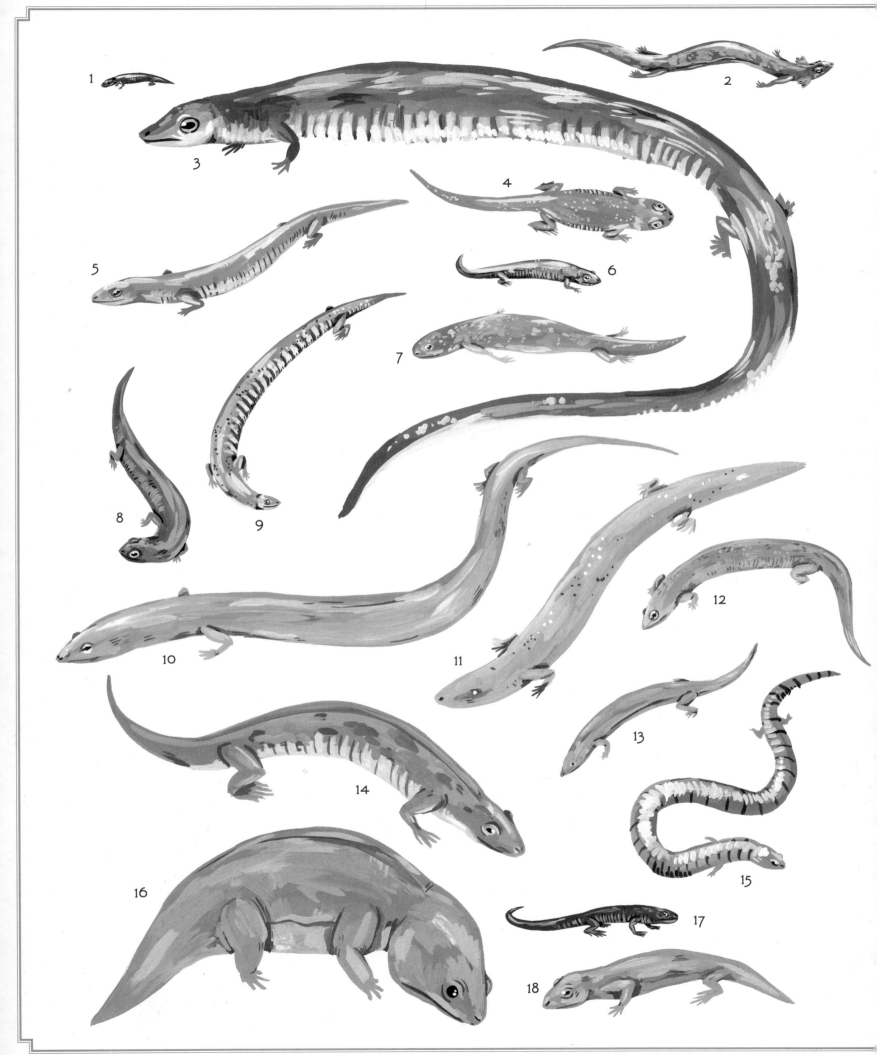

PREHISTORIC CREATURES OF THE ORDER | MICROSAURIA

MICROSAURIA

LATE CARBONIFEROUS TO EARLY PERMIAN

The microsaurs were a relatively short-lived group of amphibian-like creatures that lived both on land and in the water. With their long, muscular tails and distinctive short legs, they thrived in aquatic environments. Among their ranks were diggers, terrestrial hunters and aquatic chasers. Some species never left the water throughout their whole lives and so kept their gills in adulthood. In recent years, many scientists have started to question whether the microsaurs should be considered a separate order of life. It may be that eventually the creatures of this group end up being moved into a different order of very similar amphibian-like creatures.

Llistrofus pricei

1. LLISTROFUS PRICEI

Unlike other microsaurs, an important bone in the jaw of *Llistrofus pricei* was comparatively tiny. This was probably to make space for their extra-powerful jaw muscles.

2. MICROBRACHIS PELIKANI

Microbrachis pelikani had more vertebrae than most microsaurs, making its body look long and thin. It may have swum like an eel, chasing small shrimp-like crustaceans to eat. Like the modern-day axolotl, this microsaur kept its external fluffy gills into adulthood.

Microbrachis pelikani

3. MICRAROTER ERYTHROGEOIS

Micraroter erythrogeois had more than 20 cone-shaped teeth and a long, slender body. Like many others of its close family, *Micraroter erythrogeois* is likely to lived in aquatic environments.

4. CARROLLA CRADDOCKI

Carrolla craddocki pushed its way through hard soils, searching for burying invertebrates on which it fed. This was one of the last remaining microsaurs, likely to have been killed off by an extinction event called the Great Dying, 252 million years ago.

5. ALTENGLANERPETON SCHROEDERI

The small eyes and lack of a lateral line (special sensory organs) suggest that *Altenglanerpeton schroederi* was not a water dweller, but lived in soil. By undulating its long, thin body like a fish, it may have been able to burrow through soil and leaf litter, powering itself forward with a strong, triangle-shaped skull.

6. HYLOPLESION LONGICOSTATUM

Though only the size of a salamander, the jaws of *Hyloplesion longicostatum* could pack a punch. Within them were two sharp canines, which may have helped to grip prey. Scientists are unsure whether this species could walk on land.

Hyloplesion longicostatum

7. CARDIOCEPHALUS PEABODYI

Cardiocephalus peabodyi had a single row of cone-shaped teeth that were probably used to snap up worm-like creatures. When it was first discovered in 1910, scientists didn't know if it was an early reptile or an early amphibian.

8. BATROPETES FRITSCHI

This tiny microsaur measured only about 8 cm (3 in) in length – so small that it probably competed with insects and crustaceans for food. *Batropetes fritschi* had armour-plating on its lower side, suggesting it was regularly attacked by predators from below.

9. RHYNCHONKOS STOVALLI

With its tough, bullet-shaped skull *Rhynchonkos stovalli* looked so much like modern-day caecilians that scientists once thought they were part of the same group. This is an example of convergent evolution, where unrelated animals come to look similar after adapting to a similar way of life.

Pelodosotis elongatum

10. PELODOSOTIS ELONGATUM

With 45 vertebrae, *Pelodosotis elongatum* is likely to have been the longest microsaur, approaching 50 cm (19 in) or more. Its powerful legs allowed it to move across land with relative ease, although it probably dragged parts of its underside and tail as it walked.

11. QUASICAECILIA TEXANA

Quasicaecilia texana was a digging microsaur that may have resembled modern-day caecilians. The species' name comes from a fossil collected in Texas, USA – a skull just 2 cm (1 in) long, with a strange, shovel-shaped snout used for pushing through soil.

12. NANNAROTER MCKINZIEI

Nannaroter mckinziei was only discovered by fossil-hunters in 2008. At just 10 cm (4 in) long, this was one of the smallest digging microsaurs. It had a spade-like skull with a pointed snout. *Nannaroter mckinziei* is thought to have hunted soil invertebrates in early Permian forests.

Kirktonecta milnerae

13. KIRKTONECTA MILNERAE

Discovered and named in 2002, *Kirktonecta milnerae* is the earliest known microsaur. Its long tail fin and impressive number of vertebrae suggests that this may have been a fish-like microsaur capable of side-to-side movement through the water.

14. TUDITANUS PUNCTULATUS

With its powerful limbs, *Tuditanus punctulatus* was a land-living microsaur able to scuttle across trees and low-lying plants. It had more than 50 sharp and pointed teeth, which may have been used to stop insects from escaping once gripped by its jaws.

15. ODONTERPETON TRIANGULARIS

Known only from a single fossil, discovered in 310 million-year-old rocks from Ohio, USA, *Odonterpeton triangularis* may have had sharp, backward pointing teeth, suggesting it hunted fast-moving prey in the water.

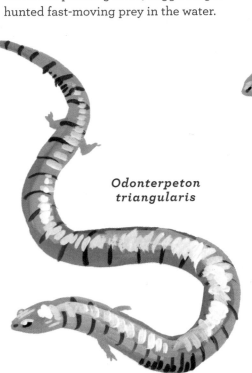

Odonterpeton triangularis

16. PANTYLUS CORDATUS

This may be the most land-adapted known microsaur. It had strong, well-built legs with a rigid skeleton and it may have been able to move with speed to escape the attentions of Permian predators, including temnospondyls.

17. UTAHERPETON FRANKLINI

At just 8 cm (3 in) long, *Utaherpeton franklini* puts the 'micro' in 'microsaur'. This salamander-like creature likely inhabited swamps and ponds, though it may have been able to move around on land for short periods. It is one of the earliest microsaurs known to scientists.

Utaherpeton franklini

18. SAXONERPETON GEINITZI

Like many amphibians, *Saxonerpeton geinitzi* appears to have had special sensory organs that helped it to detect sudden changes in water pressure that signalled approaching prey or predators. This makes it likely that it spent most of its time in water.

Saxonerpeton geinitzi

FIGURE 1. CAECILIAN

Modern-day amphibians mostly come in two shapes – the salamander-like tailed amphibians and the frog-shaped tailless amphibians. But there is a mysterious third group – the caecilians. Caecilians are limbless amphibians that usually live hidden under the ground or buried within stream beds. Fossils of caecilians are incredibly rare, so we know very little about their history or how they evolved. For many years, some scientists argued that caecilians were, in fact, a surviving part of the Microsauria order because they look so spectacularly similar. Today, most scientists disagree with this. Instead, they claim that caecilians look like some microsaurs because they became adapted to the same underwater and underground way of life.

Caecilian

FIGURE 2. MICROSAUR SKULLS

Microsaurs had skulls that were narrow, triangle-shaped and resemble those of modern-day salamanders in many ways. Their teeth were slightly curved, suggesting most microsaur species were predators. In burrowing species, the head was more bullet-shaped, so it could force its way through sand, soil and mud. Unlike many modern-day amphibians, such as frogs, there is no evidence that their larvae underwent a metamorphosis. In other words, the babies resembled the adults.

Microsaur *skull from below, showing a bullet-shaped head*

Microsaur *skull, showing curved teeth*

ICHTHYOSAURIA

EARLY TRIASSIC TO LATE CRETACEOUS

Ichthyosaurs were made famous by Victorian scientists and fossil hunters who marvelled at how similar to dolphins these reptiles were. This order includes tiny creatures that were no bigger than average-sized fish and large creatures, as big as some whales. The rise and fall of ichthyosaurs has been a subject of much debate among scientists. Peaking in the Jurassic period, species numbers dwindled during the Cretaceous period. Their extinction took place 30 million years before the end of the age of dinosaurs, for reasons currently unknown.

1. PLATYPTERYGIUS LONGMANI

Platypterygius longmani reached a length of about 7 m (23 ft). It was one of the most successful ichthyosaurs of the Cretaceous period, and among the last ichthyosaurs to live before their mysterious extinction.

2. EXCALIBOSAURUS COSTINI

The so-called 'Excalibur's lizard' had a long, pointed upper jaw that resembled that of a swordfish. This may have been whipped at shoals of fish, momentarily stunning them before swallowing them.

3. SHASTASAURUS PACIFICUS

Unlike many ichthyosaurs, *Shastasaurus pacificus* had a dolphin-like beak and no teeth. This strange adaptation may have meant that it sucked prey into its mouth by suddenly opening its jaws very wide, similar to many sharks.

4. STENOPTERYGIUS QUADRISCISSUS

Stenopterygius quadriscissus was an athletic predator of the open seas, with a cruising speed of 60 km/h (37 mph) or more. It gave birth to live babies. Scientists know this because one famous fossil shows a female *Stenopterygius* with a baby still preserved inside its womb.

Ichthyosaurus anningae

5. ICHTHYOSAURUS ANNINGAE

Ichthyosaurus anningae was named in 2015 after scientists rediscovered an unusual fossil in a museum. The name referred to Victorian fossil hunter, Mary Anning, whose spectacular fossil finds helped scientists understand the concept of extinction.

Mixosaurus cornalianus

6. MIXOSAURUS CORNALIANUS

Though lacking in size, *Mixosaurus cornalianus* had immensely powerful jaws, which it used to crush prey. The name, which means, 'mixed lizard', refers to the fact that it has features of both early and later, more dolphin-like ichthyosaurians.

7. TEMNODONTOSAURUS PLATYODON

Temnodontosaurus platyodon had the biggest eyes of any animal that has ever lived. In one fossil specimen, the eyeballs were 26 cm (10 in) in diameter – about the same size as a pumpkin.

8. CAYPULLISAURUS BONAPARTEI

Reaching nearly 5 m (16 ft), *Caypullisaurus bonapartei* was a close relative of the big-eyed ichthyosaurs, like *Ophthalmosaurus*. Even though it reached an impressive size, it may not have been the apex predator of its age.

9 ICHTHYOSAURUS COMMUNIS

This species was first discovered by Mary Anning in the 1800s, and hundreds of fossils have since been found. Some fossils are very well preserved, revealing that it had a fleshy, shark-like dorsal fin and a powerful tail.

Ichthyosaurus communis

10. EURHINOSAURUS LONGIROSTRIS

The upper jaw of *Eurhinosaurus longirostris* was twice as long as its lower jaw, which had sawfish-like teeth. *Eurhinosaurus longirostris* may have used this strange bill to search for prey in sand or seaweed.

11. NANNOPTERYGIUS ENTHEKIODON

Nannopterygius enthekiodon was named for its wing-like pectoral fins that were common to many ichthyosaurs. These fins acted like the aerofoils of an aeroplane, preventing the head from being pulled downwards through gravity and directing momentum forwards.

Nannopterygius enthekiodon

12. DEARCMHARA SHAWCROSSI

Described from only a handful of fossil bones, *Dearcmhara shawcrossi* cruised tropical lagoons in search of prey. Its fin bones suggest it may have been well adapted for speed, either to chase after fish or escape from hungry pliosaurs.

13. CYMBOSPONDYLUS NATANS

This ichthyosaur had a 1-m-(3-ft)-long skull that contained rows of sharp teeth for pinning down fish and squid-like belemnites. Like modern-day sea snakes, *Cymbospondylus natans* would have moved its long tail from side-to-side to travel through the water.

14. SHONISAURUS SIKANNIENSIS

Shonisaurus sikanniensis was a giant. With a body length approaching 21 m (69 ft), it was among the largest marine reptiles ever to have lived. It probably lacked a dorsal fin, and steadied itself using narrow, paddle-like limbs.

Malawania anachronus

15. MALAWANIA ANACHRONUS

Malawania anachronus was one of the last surviving members of the ichthyosaur order. It shared many features with earlier ichthyosaurs, which made it a 'living fossil', swimming alongside other impressively adapted ichthyosaurians of the Cretaceous period.

16. WAHLISAURUS MASSARAE

This 2-m-(7-ft)-long ichthyosaur was only discovered in 2016 after scientists carefully re-examined fossils in a museum and came to the conclusion it was a new species. Since then, a second fossil has been discovered in another collection.

Wahlisaurus massarae

17. THALATTOARCHON SAUROPHAGIS

This was the first marine reptile in the Triassic period to have evolved the status of apex predator. It may have hunted like an orca, picking out other large marine reptiles to attack.

18. BRACHYPTERYGIUS EXTREMUS

Brachypterygius extremus is known for having shorter fore limbs than other ichthyosaurs of the late Jurassic period. This suggests it might have been slower than other marine reptiles at the time.

19. OPHTHALMOSAURUSI CENICUS

Ophthalmosaurus icenicus had eyes the size of honeydew melons, which it used to hunt deep sea squid-like animals. These enormous eyeballs had special bones within them to protect them from being squashed under the water pressure in the deep ocean.

Hudsonelpidia brevirostris

20. HUDSONELPIDIA BREVIROSTRIS

Hudsonelpidia brevirostris was a mysterious micro-ichthyosaur known from a single fossil skeleton. Like other ichthyosaurs of the late Triassic period, *Hudsonelpidia brevirostris* had a mix of primitive and more evolved features, such as a powerful tail.

FIGURE 1. ICHTHYOSAUR FOSSIL

Ichthyosaurs gave birth in the water to live young. Many fossils show the baby embryos inside them and some fossils even show babies that were in the process of being born. Early ichthyosaurs gave birth to babies head first, but in the later stages of their evolution, it seems that the babies came out tail-first. Being born tail-first meant that the babies could swim to the surface straight away after being born to take their first breath. Fossils of early whales suggest marine mammals also came through a similar evolution, from head-first to tail-first birth.

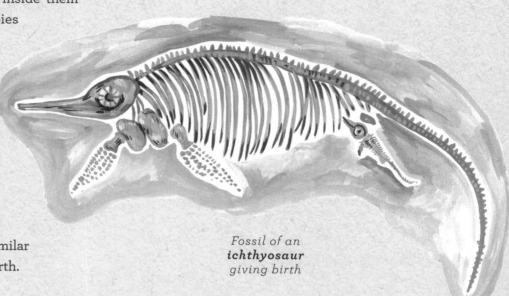

Fossil of an **ichthyosaur** *giving birth*

FIGURE 2. SQUAMATA

The scaled lizards (order Squamata) began their rise at about the same time as ichthyosaurs and plesiosaurs, and it was from them that ocean-living super-predators evolved in the late Cretaceous. These were the mosasaurs. Though many of these marine lizards measured around 4 m (13 ft) in length, some species reached lengths of 17 m (55 ft) or more. This is comparable to the largest ichthyosaurs. Mosasaurs became the apex predators of their day, but went extinct 66 million years ago. However, their squamata cousins survived, and today they live in the form of lizards and snakes, of which 10,000 living species are known.

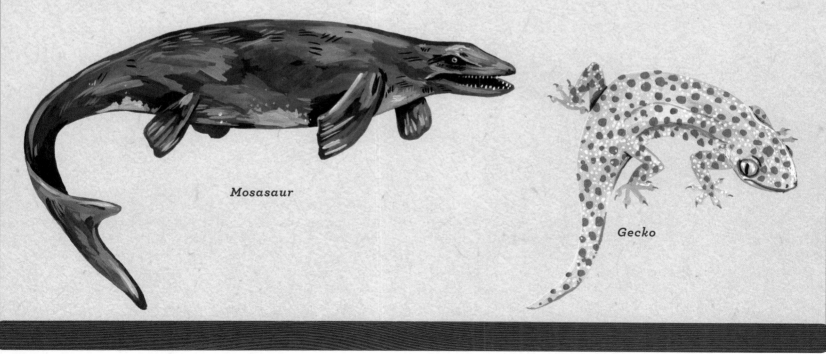

Mosasaur

Gecko

PREHISTORIC CREATURES OF THE ORDER | PTEROSAURIA

PTEROSAURIA

EARLY TRIASSIC TO LATE CRETACEOUS

Members of the order Pterosauria ruled the air for more than 150 million years. During this time, a number of pterosaur species evolved to hunt everything from insects to fish and even small dinosaurs. Their success was in part due to a flexible and powerful bone in their wing – an elongated finger from which wing-membrane was attached. Fossil finds suggest that many species of pterosaur were highly ornamented and used their colours and headcrests to show off to members of the opposite sex or to intimidate rivals who they were keen to scare away.

1. THALASSODROMEUS SETHI

The magnificent crest of *Thalassodromeus sethi* took up 75 per cent of its head. Only 1 mm (0.04 in) thick, it was paper-thin. Like other large pterosaurs, it was thought to have hunted on the ground.

2. RHAMPHORHYNCHUS MUENSTERI

Rhamphorhynchus muensteri had a long tail that ended in a diamond-shaped vane. Like modern-day aquatic birds, it may have dived into the water to chase fish, propelling itself through the water using its broad feet.

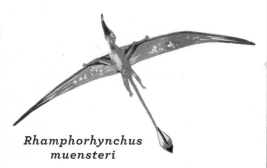

Rhamphorhynchus muensteri

3. COLOBORHYNCHUS CAPITO

Coloborhynchus capito is the largest pterosaur known to have teeth. Its impressive skull measured 75 cm (30 in) and its wingspan was 7 m (23 ft), more than twice that of the largest bird alive today.

Darwinopterus modularis

4. DARWINOPTERUS MODULARIS

Darwinopterus modularis had features of the earliest long-tailed pterosaurs and the later short-tailed pterosaurs that dominated in the Cretaceous period. For this reason, *Darwinopterus modularis* is often called a 'transitional fossil' between the two types of pterosaur.

5. HATZEGOPTERYX THAMBEMA

Hatzegopteryx thambema is likely to have had the longest skull of any land animal that has ever lived. *Hatzegopteryx thambeta* was an apex predator, which may even have hunted and killed small dinosaurs.

6. PTERANODON LONGICEPS

With around 1,200 fossils discovered, *Pteranodon longiceps* is the pterosaur that scientists know the most about. Male *Pteranodons* were much larger than females, and may have fought one another to guard groups of females, just as seals do today.

7. JEHOLOPTERUS NINCHENGENSIS

Jeholopterus ninchengensis had strong wings with long, curved claws. Though its close family were insect hunters, *Jeholopterus ninchengensis* was larger and more powerful – about the size of a seagull. Some scientists think it may have been capable of pulling fish from out of the water.

Jeholopterus ninchengensis

8. TUPUXUARA LONGICRISTATUS

Close examination of the fossilised eyeballs of *Tupuxuara longicristatus* suggest that it was a day-hunting pterosaur. Some argue that it may have been omnivorous, supplementing its diet with fruit as well as meat.

9. DIMORPHODON MACRONYX

This stocky pterosaur had impressive teeth and powerful snapping jaws. Unusually for pterosaurs, *Dimorphodon macronyx* had two types of teeth. Four or five of the teeth were fang-like, whereas the rest were flat, with a spearhead-like point.

10. ANUROGNATHUS AMMONI

This tiny pterosaur had a short head with pin-like teeth, which it used to snap insects out of the air. Compared to its close relatives, *Anurognathus ammoni* had a short tail that helped it manoeuvre through the forest canopy.

Anurognathus ammoni

11. QUETZALCOATLUS NORTHROPI

This was perhaps the most formidable pterosaur. On the ground, it could walk upon its claws and it stood 3 m (10 ft) tall. *Quetzalcoatlus northropi* is likely to have stalked reptiles on the ground, lunging after prey.

12. SORDES PILOSUS

The jaws of *Sordes pilosus* were filled with two kinds of teeth – pointed and flat, for tearing and crushing. A well-preserved fossil was the first to show scientists that many pterosaurs had hair-like fuzz covering their bodies.

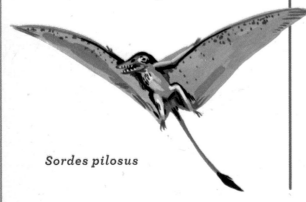

Sordes pilosus

Nemicolopterus crypticus

13. NEMICOLOPTERUS CRYPTICUS

Nemicolopterus crypticus was one of the smallest pterosaurs, with a wingspan not much larger than that of a sparrow. In fact, *Nemicolopterus* fossils are so tiny that sometimes scientists mistake them as baby pterosaurs of other species.

14. NYCTOSAURUS GRACILIS

Nyctosaurus gracilis had an antler-like structure that grew from the back of it head, which is was thought to have been used to show off its health. In some specimens, this crest measured three times longer than the head itself.

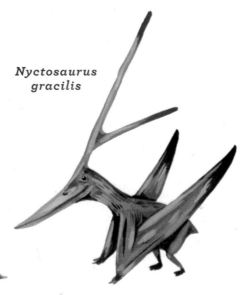

Nyctosaurus gracilis

15. PREONDACTYLUS BUFFARINII

Unlike other pterosaurs of its age, *Preondactylus buffarinii* was an excellent flyer with a wingspan matching that of a modern-day starling. Its slightly pointed teeth suggest that it mainly fed upon large insects, but it may also have hunted small fish.

16. TAPEJARA WELLNHOFERI

Tapejara wellnhoferi had a semicircular crest over the snout, which connected to a bony prong behind the head. These were likely used to help species recognise one another, but may also have helped *Tapejara* show off.

17. ARAMBOURGIANIA PHILADELPHIAE

In the air, it is likely that *Arambourgiania philadelphiae* had a 10-m-(33-ft)-long wingspan. Yet on the ground its long neck meant it would have stood face-to-face with a modern-day giraffe.

Pterodaustro guinazui

18. PTERODAUSTRO GUINAZUI

Pterodaustro guinazui had bristle-like teeth, which it used to sieve tiny crustaceans and algae from the water. Modern filter-feeding creatures, such as flamingos, develop a pink colour from this diet. It may have been the same for *Pterodaustro guinazui*.

19. TUPANDACTYLUS IMPERATOR

Like *Tapejara wellnohofferi*, this Brazilian pterosaur also possessed a giant headdress that may have helped species recognise one another. Many scientists suspect *Tupandactylus imperator* was a fish-eater that sailed over the sea on wings which spanned 5 m (16 ft).

20. PTERODACTYLUS ANTIQUUS

Many people know this as the classic 'pterodactyl', meaning 'wing finger'. It was the first pterosaur named by Victorian scientists, who correctly identified that it was a flying reptile. It was about the size of a large bat.

FIGURE 1. PTEROSAURIAN WINGS

Pterosauria was the first order of vertebrates to take to the skies. The main wing membrane attached to an extremely long fourth finger. At first, scientists considered this to be little more than a flap of skin, but a number of recent fossils have shown them to be far more complex. Within the wing membrane were strings of fibres called actinofibrils, which provided strength and flexibility during flight. The membranes also contained muscles and a network of looping blood vessels. Like bats and birds, pterosaurs had incredibly light bones that allowed them to stay in the air for longer, so using less energy.

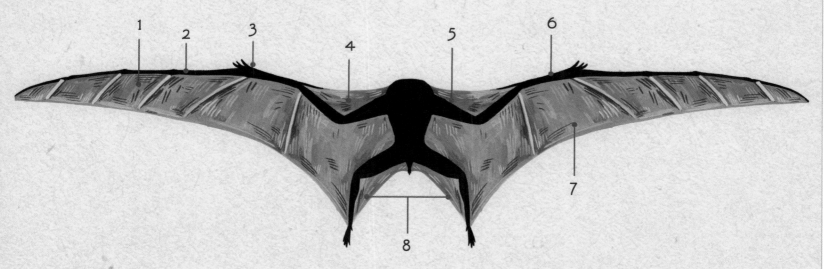

1. *Brachiopatagium*
2. *Elongated fourth finger*
3. *Three shorter fingers*
4. *Propatagium*
5. *Humerus*
6. *Forearm*
7. *Membrane*
8. *Uropatagium*

FIGURE 2. ALBATROSS

Today, in the order Procellariiformes, there is a group of birds that have adapted to a way of life not unlike that of the fish-eating pterosaurs that lived millions of years ago. They are the albatrosses. Albatrosses have huge wingspans and fly over the ocean, capable of gliding for long distances without a single beat of their wings. Just like many pterosaurs, these birds nest today in large communities on cliffs away from predators. It may even be that, like albatrosses, some pterosaurs pairbonded (formed an exclusive mating partnership) and reared their babies on the same cliffs each year.

Albatross *and chick*

PREHISTORIC CREATURES OF THE ORDER | PLESIOSAURIA

PLESIOSAURIA

LATE TRIASSIC TO EARLY CRETACEOUS

So far, more than a hundred species of plesiosaurs and pliosaurs have been discovered, making this one of the best-known orders of Mesozoic marine reptiles. This was an order of life that became one of the most fearsome groups of predators the world had ever known. Within their ranks were the sub group of short-necked, long-faced carnivores known as pliosaurs, some of whom would have rivalled today's whales in size had they not faced extinction 66 million years ago. Their fossils are found throughout the world.

Plesiosaurus dolichodeirus

1. PLESIOSAURUS DOLICHODEIRUS

Plesiosaurus dolichodeirus hit the headlines after fossil-hunter Mary Anning dug up a complete fossil skeleton in 1823. From this and other fossil finds, it was discovered that these large reptiles existed 208–55 million years ago.

2. ELASMOSAURUS PLATYURUS

Elasmosaurus platyurus may have had the longest neck of any bony creature that has ever lived. On top of its 7-cm-(3-in)-long neck was a set of snapping jaws, filled with fang-like teeth, to strike at passing prey.

3. CRYPTOCLIDUS EURYMERUS

Cryptoclidus eurymerus may have used its long, interlocking teeth like a sieve to strain small prey from the water. *Cryptoclidus* means 'hidden clavicles'. All of the plesiosaurians in this group of species possess incredibly small clavicles (collarbones).

4. ATTENBOROSAURUS CONYBEARI

Unfortunately, the most celebrated fossil of *Attenborosaurus conybeari* was destroyed during the Second World War. The fossil included skin impressions that showed that this Plesiosaurian was smooth-skinned like a dolphin.

5. POLYCOTYLUS LATIPINNIS

A fossil skeleton of an adult *Polycotylus latippinis,* discovered in the 1980s, was the first to show the tiny skeleton of an unborn embryo growing within it. This is evidence that plesiosaurians gave birth to live babies.

6. THALASSIODRACON HAWKINSI

Thalassiodracon hawkinsi had an impressive set of spear-like teeth, used for snatching at prey. Within each of its large eyes was a ring of bone that prevented damage under the crushing water pressure in the deep.

7. TRINACROMERUM KIRKI

With its long flippers, *Trinacromerum kirki* resembled a four-flippered penguin. These flippers undoubtedly improved the speed with which this sleek predator could swim. Its pointed teeth suggest that it was a specialist hunter of fish and other fast-swimming, soft-bodied creatures.

Trinacromerum kirki

8. THALASSOMEDON HANINGTONI

Evidence from fossil finds tell us that *Thalassomedon haningtoni* sometimes swallowed stones from the seabed. These stones may have helped it grind up food, or acted as ballast (heavy matter), allowing it to dive deeper with little effort.

9. RHOMALEOSAURUS CRAMPTONI

This aptly named 'strong lizard' was probably the largest apex predator of the early Jurassic seas. By forcing water through special corridors in its skull containing sensory organs, it could pick up the scents of potential prey.

10. MEYERASAURUS MORTUNERIA VICTOR

Meyerasaurus victor represented one of the earliest pliosaurs: a group that would later evolve to become monstrous hunters of other Plesiosaurians. Its teeth were smooth and unable to chew, so it likely swallowed prey whole.

Meyerasaurus mortuneria victor

11. KRONOSAURUS QUEENSLANDICUS

This pliosaur was one of the largest marine predators of all time. Its teeth could be up to 30 cm (12 in) long and were thought to be almost fang-like. Fossils of its stomach contents suggest that it may have hunted other plesiosaurians and sharks.

Microcleidus homalospondylus

12. MICROCLEIDUS HOMALOSPONDYLUS

Measuring 3 m (10 ft) in length, *Microcleidus homalospondylus* was about as big as a medium-sized dolphin. Like other species of this order, it had large eyes for spotting prey and a long snout filled with needle-like teeth.

13. MORTUNERIA SEYMOURENSIS

This is the best known filter-feeding plesiosaurian. By scooping up mouthfuls of sand and forcing water and sediment out of its jaws, *Morturneria seymourensis* could sieve small crustaceans and other tiny bottom-dwellers in its teeth before swallowing them.

14. STYXOSAURUS SNOWII

Almost half of *Styxosaurus snowii*'s 12-m-(39-ft)-long body was taken up with its neck. Its cone-shaped teeth were used to pin down slippery prey, stopping them from escaping so that they could be swallowed whole.

15. LEPTOCLEIDUS CAPENSIS

Unlike other pliosaurs, *Leptocleidus capensis* hunted in shallow lagoons and estuaries. Like the modern-day bull shark, it may also have occasionally been found in rivers. Why it evolved to colonise these habitats is unknown.

16. HAUFFIOSAURUS LONGIROSTRIS

Compared to other creatures in this order, *Hauffiosaurus zanoni* had a longer and more pointed snout, filled with particularly slender teeth that were very good at piercing soft prey. It probably fed on a diet of fish.

17. WESTPHALIASAURUS SIMONSENSII

This 4-m-(15-ft)-long Plesiosaurian is known from an almost complete fossil skeleton. Unfortunately, no fossil skull has been found, meaning that scientists don't yet know what the head of *Westphaliasaurus* looked like.

18. MURAENOSAURUS LEEDSI

Muraenosaurus leedsi's incredibly long neck made up half of its body length. Some scientists think this may have been for sneaking up on unwary prey, while others argue that it was used to scoop up creatures from the sea floor.

19. ATYCHODRACON MEGACEPHALUS

A spectacular museum specimen of *Atychodracon megacephalus* was destroyed during the Second World War. Thankfully, photography archives exist, so scientists can continue to learn about it. This pliosaur had a disproportionately large head, so much so that 'megacephalus' directly translates as 'big head'.

20. LIOPLEURODON FEROX

Liopleurodon ferox was an apex predator that lived in the Jurassic seas, 160 million years ago. Its long, paddle-like limbs were built for speed, and fossils of its skull show that it could sniff out potential prey in the water.

FIGURE 1. PLESIOSAUR SKELETON

Plesiosaurs had a broad, flattened body and a short tail. Within their limbs were distinctive reptilian limb bones, providing evidence that these were once land creatures that took to the sea, rather like whales and ichthyosaurs. The reason for the extremely long neck of some plesiosaurs has been debated for many years. In many species, the long neck and biting jaws may have been used to help the plesiosaur lunge into schools of fish. It is thought that some species used them to sweep over the sea floor looking for buried animals.

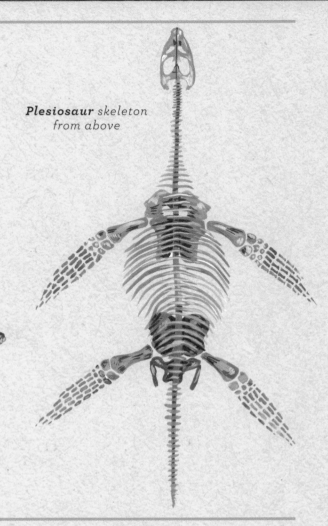

Plesiosaur skeleton
from above

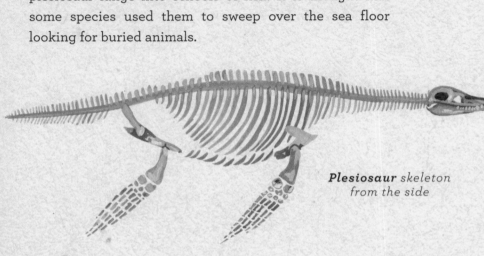

Plesiosaur skeleton
from the side

FIGURE 2. LEATHERBACK TURTLE

In the late Triassic, another group of reptiles were taking to the seas. These were the earliest turtles (order Testudines) and they would form an order that, unlike plesiosaurs, would survive to the modern day. Turtles live throughout the world in marine and freshwater, and many species (commonly called tortoises) have taken to the land completely. Nearly all testudines are known for their hardened shells, made up of 60 bones that are made from parts of their backbone and ribs. Small parts of the order became shell-less. They include the leatherback turtles, a marine group that evolved in the last days of dinosaurs. Only one leatherback turtle species lives today, *Dermochelys coriacea*. This marine giant regularly reaches a length of 2 m (7 ft) from head to tail.

Leatherback turtle

ORNITHISCHIA

EARLY JURASSIC TO LATE CRETACEOUS

The ornithischians were dinosaurs known for their bird-like hips. Among their ranks were the horned dinosaurs, which included *Tricerotops*, the duck-billed dinosaurs like *Edmontosaurus* and dinosaurs with sharp spines and body armour, including *Stegosaurus*. Many ornithischians were herbivores and at least some are likely to have moved in great herds. In the last few years, some scientists have argued that the two traditional orders of dinosaur – the Saurischia and Ornithischia – may not be as accurate as we first thought, with far more diversity within these orders. In the future, these dinosaurs may be categorised in a different way.

Fruitadens haagarorum

1. FRUITADENS HAAGARORUM

Weighing little more than a rabbit, *Fruitadens haagarorum* is the smallest ornithischian ever found. It was built for speed, and could sprint on its muscular hind legs, probably to avoid being eaten.

2. CHASMOSAURUS BELLI

Chasmosaurus means 'opening lizard', which refers to the window-like pattern of bones in this dinosaur's delicate neck frill. These were probably not used for defence, and scientists suspect they used them to show off to one another.

3. TRICERATOPS HORRIDUS

With a 2-m-(7-ft)-skull, *Triceratops horridus* may have had the biggest head of any land animal. Its neck frill and three horns may have been used for defence, although many scientists believe that they could have been used for showing off.

4. LESOTHOSAURUS DIAGNOSTICUS

For its size, *Lesothosaurus diagnosticus* had huge eyes. Fossils showing wear and tear on its teeth suggest that it wasn't a strict herbivore, and may have eaten small reptiles and insects as well.

5. MICROCERATUS GOBIENSIS

With a body length of just 60 cm (24 in), *Microceratus gobiensis* was one of the smallest ornithischians. Though it walked on two legs, it possessed the same bony neck frill and sharp, beak-like mouths as its relatives, like *Triceratops*.

Microceratus gobiensis

6. IGUANODON BERNISSARTENSIS

This bulky herbivore's long thumb spikes may have been used to defend against predators. As it grew older and heavier, *Iguanodon bernissartensis* may have depended more and more on four-legged movement.

Liaoningosaurus paradoxus

7. LIAONINGOSAURUS PARADOXUS

Liaoningosaurus paradoxus was unique among armoured dinosaurs because it ate meat – with fossils of its stomach contents suggesting that it ate fish. It seemed to possess armour underneath its body, suggesting that it could swim through predator-infested waters.

8. HUAYANGOSAURUS TAIBAII

Twenty million years before *Stegosaurus stenops* there lived *Huayangosaurus taibaii*. This dinosaur was 4.5 m (14.7 ft) long from head to tail and rather than having spiny plates, its body armour was covered with spikes.

9. ORYCTODROMEUS CUBICULARIS

Oryctodromeus cubicularis, meaning 'digging runner', is one of the only known digging dinosaurs. It had powerful forearms, which it used to dig underground dens. A fast and agile herbivore, it lived in the shadows of predatory tyrannosaurs.

Protoceratops andrewsi

10. PROTOCERATOPS ANDREWSI

A large number of *Protoceratops andrewsi* fossils were found in the region that became modern-day Mongolia. The griffin – a mythical creature – may have been inspired by the strange, bird-like fossil skulls that were discovered by early humans.

11. EDMONTOSAURUS ANNECTENS

This duck-billed ornithischian possessed an extra-wide muzzle that helped it pluck leaves, and rows of tough teeth for chewing. Like all duck-billed dinosaurs, *Edmontosaurus annectens* could walk on two legs. Special air-sacs in its nostrils may have been used for calling to members of its herd.

Hypsilophodon foxii

12. HYPSILOPHODON FOXII

Hypsilophodon foxii was built to run, with a sleek skeleton and a long, tendon-filled tail that helped it balance. Like most ornithischians, *Hypsilophodon foxii* had a small beak.

13. EUOPLOCEPHALUS TUTUS

Euoplocephalus tutus was an armoured powerhouse, weighing more than 2,500 kg (3 t). Covered with shield-like plates, this dinosaur had a heavy tail club that could break the fragile legs and arms of predators.

14. LAMBEOSAURUS LAMBEI

This duck-billed dinosaur had a distinctive hollow skull crest that pointed upwards. It may have used this device to make loud calls to entice members of the opposite sex.

Psittacosaurus mongoliensis

15. PSITTACOSAURUS MONGOLIENSIS

Psittacosaurus mongoliensis was a parrot-like Cretaceous dinosaur, with a tall skull and a hard beak for snipping leaves off branches. It is thought to have been a very social creature, roaming through dense forests in family groups.

16. STEGOSAURUS STENOPS

The giant bony plates on *Stegosaurus stenops* were once thought to be armour, but blood vessels discovered within them suggest that they caused these dinosaurs to blush red. This might have helped *Stegosaurus stenops* to communicate, or perhaps stay cool.

Stegoceras validum

17. STEGOCERAS VALIDUM

Though it was little more than the size of a goat, *Stegoceras validum* could certainly pack a punch. Its heavily domed skull with armoured ridges could be used as a battering ram to scare off predators or rivals.

18. KOSMOCERATOPS RICHARDSONI

Fossils of this dinosaur's skull tell us that it was covered in horns on the back of its head, nose, and cheeks. Unusually, scientists think that both males and females possessed this impressively ornate headgear.

19. PARASAUROLOPHUS CYRTOCRISTATUS

Parasaurolophus cyrtocristatus had a hollow, bony crest that was almost 1 m (3 ft) long. Once thought to be a snorkel, this strange device was probably used to amplify hoots and other special calls, particularly during breeding season.

20. SCELIDOSAURUS HARRISONII

This lizard-like ornithiscian is one of the earliest dinosaurs for which a complete fossil skeleton exists. It fed upon low scrubby branches and had a large gut to digest food.

Scelidosaurus harrisonii

FIGURE 1. ORNITHISCHIAN HIP BONE

When Victorian scientists first looked at fossils of dinosaur bones, they noticed that their hips came in two styles. In one group of dinosaurs – the Saurischia group – a specific bone in the hip, called the 'pubis', pointed towards the head. In the other group – the ornithischian group – the pubis pointed down and towards the back of the body. The Ornithischians had hips similar to modern-day birds, hence the name for this order, the 'bird-hipped dinosaurs'.

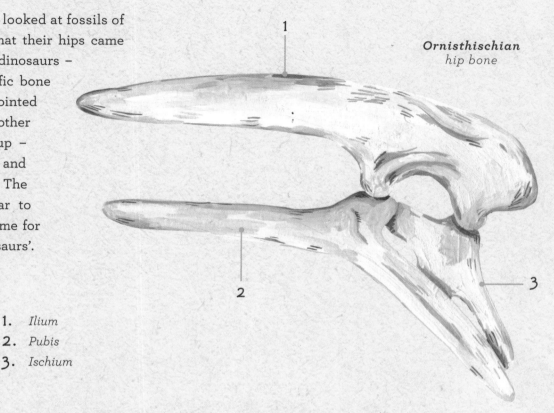

Ornisthischian
hip bone

1. *Ilium*
2. *Pubis*
3. *Ischium*

FIGURE 2. ORDER CROCODILIA

Apart from birds, the crocodilians (order Crocodilia) are the closest living relatives of dinosaurs. Quite how crocodiles survived the meteorite impact and the intense volcanic activity going on at the time remains a mystery. However, two factors may be part of the secret behind their survival. Crocodiles have a low metabolism and can last for long periods without food. Many crocodiles are also capable of hibernating, something scientists think dinosaurs were not able to do. Fossil finds suggest that this impressive order evolved in the late Cretaceous period, 83.5 million years ago. Today, 23 crocodilian species live in tropical zones all over the world.

Nile crocodile

SAURISCHIA

LATE TRIASSIC TO LATE CRETACEOUS (EXCLUDING BIRDS)

Among the saurischians (order Saurischia) are the meat-eating dinosaurs that walked on two legs (theropods) and the giant, long-necked herbivores (sauropods) that include the largest and heaviest animals that have ever walked the Earth. The order was named in 1888, when Victorian scientists first noticed that many dinosaurs had lizard-like hips (see p. 49). At the time, it was thought that this similarity meant that these dinosaurs were all close family relations. More recently, however, scientists have started to question this. In the future, there is a possibility that these dinosaurs will be sorted into new, different orders.

Magyarosaurus dacus

1. MAGYAROSAURUS DACUS

Magyarosaurus dacus was a dwarf sauropod, measuring just over 6 m (20 ft) in length. The small size of this species is likely a result of island dwarfing, where marooned individuals of a species evolve to be a smaller size.

2. HALSZKARAPTOR ESCUILLIEI

This swan-like dinosaur had an incredibly long neck, on top of which was a spoon-shaped skull armed with sharp, backward-pointing teeth. Like crocodiles, *Halszkaraptor escuilliei* had sensory pits on its face that may have helped detect prey underwater.

Halszkaraptor escuilliei

3. TYRANNOSAURUS REX

Tyrannosaurus rex is one of the most powerful land predators the world has ever seen. With teeth as long as bananas and powerful jaw muscles, *Tyrannosaurus rex* had a bite force unmatched by any other animal.

4. MICRORAPTOR ZHAOIANUS

This four-winged saurischian had long feathers on both its arms and legs, giving *Microraptor zhaoianus* four wings, rather than two. Like some modern-day birds, it had shimmering markings on its feathers.

Microraptor zhaoianus

5. GIGANOTOSAURUS CAROLINII

With a skull almost 2 m (7 ft) in length, *Giganotosaurus carolinii* rivals *Tyrannosaurus rex* for the title of biggest meat-eating dinosaur. It probably fed on young, long-necked dinosaurs, dominating ecosystems 98 million years ago in what is now Argentina.

Yi qi

6. YI QI

This dinosaur is named 'strange wing' in Chinese. Its long third finger had skin attached to it, forming a simple wing that resembled that of a bat wing. It is likely to have hunted small flying insects in the treetops.

7. ALLOSAURUS FRAGILIS

75 million years before *Tyrannosaurus rex,* there was a mighty predator called *Allosaurus fragilis*. Using its upper jaw like a hatchet knife, it may have ambushed unwary herbivores. Some experts believe it may have occasionally hunted in packs.

8. DIPLODOCUS LONGUS

The large size of *Diplodocus longus* may have protected it from predators like *Allosaurus fragilis,* with whom it shared its North American habitat. Fossils of its teeth suggest that it fed by stripping leaves from branches.

9. TARBOSAURUS BATAAR

With more than 60 large teeth and a rigid lower jaw capable of locking into place, *Tarbosaurus bataar* could deliver an impressive bite. Like its cousin, *Tyrannosaurus rex,* this dinosaur was an apex predator.

Archaeopteryx lithographica

10. ARCHAEOPTERYX LITHOGRAPHICA

The discovery of *Archaeopteryx lithographica* showed scientists how the first birds evolved from dinosaurs. Though it possessed jaws with sharp teeth and three-clawed fingers, this saurischian had the same broad flight feathers and lightweight skeleton of birds today.

11. DEINONYCHUS ANTIRRHOPUS

The so-called 'terrible claw' dinosaur was an impressive predator that lived in North America, 110 million years ago. Its toe claws were almost as long as a human hand, and could be used to slash and disembowel prey.

12. EORAPTOR LUNENSIS

Eoraptor lunensis, meaning 'dawn plunderer', lived 230 million years ago and was among the very first predatory dinosaurs. On each forearm were five fingers, three of which had large claws to help handle prey.

Eoraptor lunensis

13. CARNOTAURUS SASTREI

Carnotaurus sastrei's thick horns above its eyes were used during battles between rivals. Its strong neck muscles suggest it could withstand the impact of a rival's skull colliding at more than 17 km/h (11 mph).

14. COMPSOGNATHUS LONGIPES

Compsognathus longipes was a nimble, turkey-sized dinosaur capable of sprinting at great speed. The fossilised guts of some specimens tell us about their last meals before their death. These impressive fossil finds suggest that these dinosaurs hunted agile lizards.

Compsognathus longipes

15. BRACHIOSAURUS ALTITHORAX

Brachiosaurus altithorax's short tail and long forelegs meant that it had a body that slanted downwards, away from the head. This unusual posture probably helped it to reach the juiciest leaves on the tallest branches.

16. SPINOSAURUS AEGYPTIACUS

With a body longer than most buses, *Spinosaurus aegyptiacus* was among the largest known predatory dinosaurs. Its long, crocodile-like face suggests it ate fish. The function of the long spines that ran along the back are unknown.

17. ARGENTINOSAURUS HUINCULENSIS

Though only a few bones of this saurischian giant have ever been found, scientists suspect it was perhaps the largest of the long-necked dinosaurs. From head-to-tail, *Argentinosaurus huinculensis* measured almost 40 m (131 ft) and may have weighed more than 80,000 kg (80 t).

Velociraptor mongoliensis

18. VELOCIRAPTOR MONGOLIENSIS

Although hardly bigger than a turkey, the powerful jaws and large brain of *Velociraptor mongoliensis* suggests that it was among the most fearsome predators. Its feathers may have been used to help brood eggs or for speed.

19. STRUTHIOMIMUS ALTUS

This ostrich-like dinosaur was built for speed. By looking at fossils of its legs, some scientists estimate that *Struthiomimus altus* could run as fast as 80 km/h (50 mph), which is comparable to a modern-day antelope.

Struthiomimus altus

20. OVIRAPTOR PHILOCERATOPS

This was one of the most bird-like predatory dinosaurs. It likely had long feathers and a head crest used for display, just like some modern birds. Additionally, one fossil shows that they sat on their nests like birds.

Oviraptor philoceratops

FIGURE 1. SAURISCHIAN HIP BONE

Unlike the ornithischian dinosaurs, the pubis bone of saurischian dinosaurs points backwards, making it hang parallel to another bone in the hips called the 'ischium'. Not all saurischians kept these lizard-like hips, however. It seems that some groups, notably birds and the unusual theropods called therizinosaurians, went on to later evolve hips like those of ornithischians, perhaps as an adaptation to a non-meat diet.

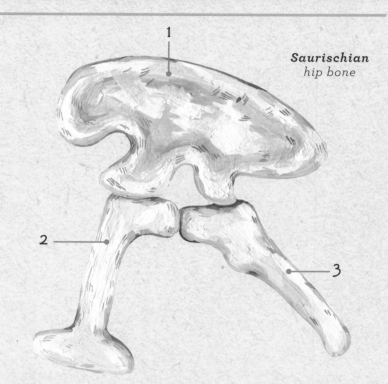

Saurischian
hip bone

1. *Ilium*
2. *Pubis*
3. *Ischium*

FIGURE 2. ARCHAEOPTERYX

Archaeopteryx is one of many fossils that have given scientists clear evidence that one small part of the saurischian order took to the skies and became the animals we know today as birds. This small Jurassic dinosaur has many features we associate with modern-day birds, including a sizeable reptilian tail, long, clawed fingers and peg-like teeth. Its wings were covered with distinctive flight feathers, like those of modern birds. The two-legged skeleton of *Archaeopteryx* puts early birds in the same group as theropod dinosaurs like *Tyrannosaurus rex* and *Allosaurus fragilis*. This makes them distantly related cousins.

Archaeopteryx
fossil

Archaeopteryx

LAMNIFORMES

EARLY CRETACEOUS TO PRESENT

After the death of dinosaurs and large marine lizards, sharks of the order Lamniformes were primed to take on the mantle of apex predator in the open seas. For many millions of years, they flourished in monstrous forms such as *Megalodon* – an 18-m-(59-ft)-long hunter of early whales that gained infamy for being the largest shark that ever lived. But *Megalodon* was just one of many lamniform sharks that flourished in the last 66 million years, and not all of them were as deadly. Some of the lamniformes were scavengers, some may have been dwellers of the deep sea and some prehistoric lamniform sharks may even have been filter-feeders.

1. CARCHAROCLES AURICULATUS

Carcharocles auriculatus is one of the earliest sharks in the so-called 'megatooth' collection of sharks. With teeth up to 11 cm (4 in) long, *Carcharocles auriculatus* was larger than a great white shark.

2. ANOMOTODON NOVUS

It is possible that *Anomotodon novus* possessed jaws that could extend from out of its mouth to snatch at passing prey. It is thought that this species may have had a long, electricity-detecting snout like modern-day goblin sharks.

Anomotodon novus

3. COSMOPOLITODUS HASTALIS

Fossils of the so-called 'broad-tooth shark' are found all over the world. This whale-eating shark's teeth were 7.5 cm (2.9 in) long. Fossils of its teeth suggest that it may have been an early ancestor of the great white shark.

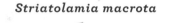

Striatolamia macrota

4. STRIATOLAMIA MACROTA

Striatolamia macrota was a sand tiger shark. Like today's bull sharks, *Striatolamia macrota* may have been able to hunt in river estuaries. Sediments from all over the world are rich with their fossil teeth.

5. CARCHAROCLES ANGUSTIDENS

Carcharocles angustidens was another early mega-tooth and relative of *Megalodon*. In 2001, a well preserved fossil of teeth and vertebrae was discovered in New Zealand. It suggested that *Carcharocles angustidens* may have been more than 9 m (29 ft) in length.

6. PSEUDOCORAX AFFINIS

In 2012, scientists noticed that some fossils of raven shark teeth were slightly smaller and pointier than others. These strange teeth represented a new species, *Pseudocorax* – the 'false raven tooth shark'.

7. OTODUS OBLIQUUS

Teeth from this enormous shark have been discovered in fossil beds around the world. Each tooth is large and backward pointing, hence its name, which means 'ear-shaped tooth'. Next to each tooth is a pair of smaller teeth called 'cusplets'.

8. CARDABIODON RICKI

One hundred million years ago, this giant shark was an apex predator that rivalled *Leptostyrax macrorhiza*. At 5.5 m (18 ft) long, with a jaw almost 1 m (3 ft) wide, it would have made short work of most creatures at the time.

9. LEPTOSTYRAX MACRORHIZA

At over 6 m (20 ft) long, this shark dwarfed most other sharks of the time. *Leptostyrax macrorhiza* was a relative of modern-day sand tiger sharks. As well as fish, it may have fed on marine reptiles, including small mosasaurs.

Leptostyrax macrorhiza

10. CARCHAROCLES MEGALODON

Reaching a length of almost 20 m (67 ft), this is the biggest shark ever discovered. With teeth the size of a human hand, and jaws capable of slicing through whale bone, there may never be a predator like this in our oceans again.

Squalicorax falcatus

11. SQUALICORAX FALCATUS

Fossils of *Squalicorax falcatus* teeth stuck in dinosaur bones show that this shark was an impressive scavenger of large land animals whose bodies had been swept out to sea. Their teeth were covered in saw-like serrations.

12. CRETOXYRHINA MANTELLI

Measuring 9 m (29 ft) in length, *Cretoxyrhina mantelli* may have been the largest shark during the age of dinosaurs. Its sharp teeth would have been used to slice up prey, including plesiosaurs and mosasaurs.

13. CRETOLAMNA APPENDICULATA

Cretolamna appendiculata survived the meteorite that killed off most of the dinosaurs. Fossils of its teeth have been found in many parts of the world, suggesting that this was a highly adaptable and competitive shark.

Cretolamna appendiculata

14. CARCHAROCLES CHUBUTENSIS

Carcharocles chubutensis is likely to have been the forerunner of *Megalodon*, according to many scientists. By studying fossils of its 10-cm-(4-in)-long teeth, scientists calculate that many individuals may have been 12 m (39 ft) or more in length.

15. CARCHARIAS TINGITANA

Little more than 1 m (2 ft) in length, *Carcharias tingitana* was a pint-sized predator that thrived in the immediate aftermath of the meteorite explosion that ended the age of dinosaurs. As food chains collapsed, larger sharks dwindled to extinction.

Carcharias tingitana

16. ALOPIAS GRANDIS

Judging by the size and shape of its fossil teeth, *Alopias grandis* may have resembled a great white shark in size and character. Scientists don't know whether it possessed the same whip-like tail as modern-day species.

17. PALAEOCARCHARODON ORIENTALIS

Rare fossils of *Palaeocarcharodon orientalis* teeth show the same steak-knife serrations as found in modern great white sharks. This has forced scientists to question whether this – the so-called 'pygmy white shark' – is its ancient ancestor.

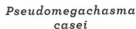

Pseudomegachasma casei

18. PSEUDOMEGACHASMA CASEI

When fossils of *Pseudomegachasma casei* were first discovered, scientists thought they were from the megamouth shark. Later, they realised they were from a new species, hence the name meaning 'false megamouth'.

19. CARCHARODON HUBBELLI

This shark shows features in common with the present day great white shark and mako shark, and fossils of this species may be an important 'missing link' between the two groups.

Isurus planus

20. ISURUS PLANUS

The unusual backwards curving teeth of *Isurus planus* gave this species the name 'hook-tooth mako shark'. *Isurus planus* was about the size of a great white shark. It likely fed upon whales, seals and, possibly, other sharks.

FIGURE 1. LAMNIFORM FEATURES

Lamniform sharks are best known for being able to maintain a higher body temperature than the surrounding water. This allows them to live in colder waters than many other sharks. Sharks of this order also have two dorsal fins, five gill slits and a mouth that extends behind the eyes, and which can open wider than most sharks, including the great white shark. Lamniform sharks also lack a protective see-through eyelid (the nictitating membrane). This means that when they bite, lamniform shark often roll their eyes backward into their sockets to protect them.

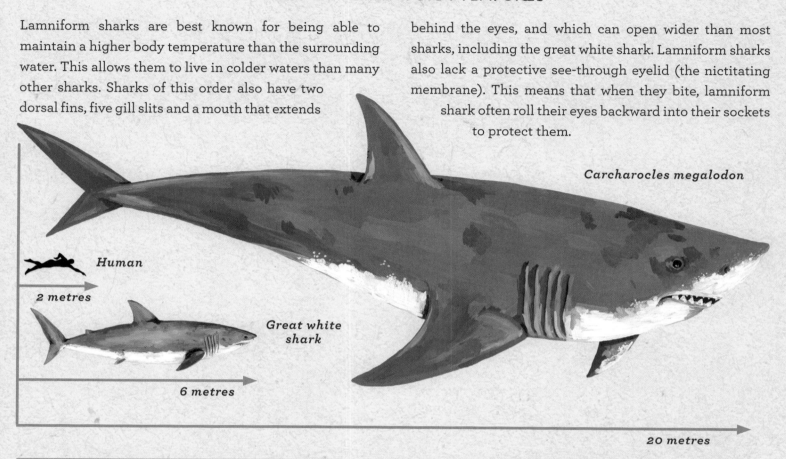

Carcharocles megalodon

Human

2 metres

Great white shark

6 metres

20 metres

FIGURE 2. GREAT WHITE SHARK

Lamniform sharks live on today through a number of surviving species, the most well-known being the great white *Carcharodon carcharias* – the largest predatory shark in existence today. The great white only reaches about a third of the size of *Carcharocles megalodon*, but it is an effective predator of seals, big fish, whales and dolphins. Though the reputation of the great white is fierce, attacks on humans are rare. Instead, it is humans who are a far greater threat to them. Each year, humans kill as many as 100 million sharks for food and sport. This is a creature whose survival is far from secure.

Great white shark

PILOSA

EARLY PALEOGENE TO PRESENT

The creatures known today as anteaters and sloths are just two remaining branches of a once-blossoming family tree that began in the years following the extinction of dinosaurs. Together with the ground sloths, they form the order Pilosa. Ground sloths were successful South American herbivores, some of which even went on to colonise North America and the Caribbean islands. Many of the larger ground sloth species were among the biggest mammalian herbivores to ever have walked the Earth. Many of these species only faced extinction in the last 10,000 years and their fossils and the remains of their tunnels are still being discovered today.

Acratocnus odontrigonus

1. ACRATOCNUS ODONTRIGONUS

Like many island sloths of the time, *Acratocnus odontrigonus* was a small, lightweight ground sloth. Its large, hooked claws and relatively small size suggest that it could alternate between living in the trees and on the ground.

2. EREMOTHERIUM EOMIGRANS

Unlike other large ground sloth species, *Eremotherium eomigrans* had five fingers on each hand. Four of these fingers were armed with sharp claws, and the largest claw was almost 30 cm (12 in) long.

3. MYLODON DARWINII

Mylodon darwinii had a thick layer of bony plates under its skin that provided extra protection. This was one of the last mainland ground sloths on Earth to face extinction – only a few thousand years ago – possibly at the hands of human hunters.

4. PARAMYLODON HARLANI

Named for American palaeontologist Dr Richard Harlan, this ground sloth was very well armoured. Underneath its skin, it had a special network of bony plates, called dermal ossicles, which were similar to those found on modern-day armadillos.

5. THALASSOCNUS YAUCENSIS

This long-nosed marine sloth was an adept swimmer. When hungry, it moved into deep waters to pull out seagrasses using its muscular lips. Like *Thalassocnus carolomartini*, this marine sloth was almost certainly a super-adapted descendent of earlier marine sloths.

6. MEGALONYX JEFFERSONII

Megalonyx (meaning 'large claw') was a ground sloth that lived across much of North America before facing extinction 10,000 years ago. It measured 3 m (10 ft) in length and may have weighed 1,000 kg (1 t). *Megalonyx jeffersonii* was, like all ground sloths, a herbivore. Fossils suggest that adults were social and cared for young family members.

7. PROTAMANDUA ROTHI

Fossils of this early anteater were first discovered in Argentina in 1896. It is likely that *Protamandua rothi* fed on colonies of ants by tearing apart their nests with its giant claws, before eating the insects inside.

Protamandua rothi

8. HAPALOPS RUETIMEYERI

Hapalops ruetimeyeri was a 1-m-(3-ft)-long ground sloth which probably spent some of its time in the treetops. Like all ground sloths, it walked on the knuckles of its forelimbs like a gorilla while moving around on the ground.

Hapalops ruetimeyeri

9. MEGATHERIUM AMERICANUM

Measuring 6 m (20 ft) from head to tail and weighing 4,000 kg (4 t), *Megatherium* is one of the largest ever land animals. Lifting itself up on its hind legs, it would have been able to reach leafy branches with its 20-cm-(8-in)-long claws. *Megatherium americanum* is thought to have been hunted to extinction 10,000 years ago.

10. ACRATOCNUS YE

This Caribbean sloth was able to dangle from upper branches using its sharp, hooked claws. Fossils of *Acratocnus ye* are known from recently explored cave systems in the Dominican Republic and Haiti.

11. THALASSOCNUS NATANS

Living six million years ago, *Thalassocnus natans* was the first species of marine sloth to be discovered. Fossils of its teeth show scratches made from chewing sand. This suggests that *Thalassocnus natans* rarely strayed far from the shoreline where it fed on a diet of seaweeds and seagrasses.

12. THINOBADISTES SEGNIS

Being an impressive swimmer, *Thinobadistes segnis* is likely to have hopped from island to island, making its way across the prehistoric seaway that once existed between North America and South America, where ground sloths evolved.

13. GLOSSOTHERIUM ROBUSTRUM

Like elephants, *Glossotherium robustrum* had unusually large ear bones that were sensitive to low frequencies. It may be that they could communicate with one another over long distances, making low sounds amplified by their large nostrils.

14. NEOTAMANDUA BOREALIS

Small fragments of fossil teeth and bone suggest that this early anteater may have grown to the enormous weight of 100 kg (220 lbs). It would likely have moved across the forest floor and climbed trees in search of ants and termites.

Neotamandua borealis

15. PALAEOMYRMIDON INCOMTUS

Known from just a single fossil skull discovered in 1907, this mouse-like anteater is most likely an ancestor of today's silky anteater. However, unlike the silky anteater, *Palaeomyrmidon incomtus* is thought to have hunted on the forest floor.

16. PROMEGATHERIUM PARVULUM

One of the earliest ground sloths, this creature lived in Argentina between 9–6.8 million years ago. It was first named from fossils discovered by palaeontologist Florentino Ameghino in 1887. Ameghino published more than 24 volumes about fossils, in which he described more than 9,000 extinct species, including this one.

Neocnus comes

17. NEOCNUS COMES

Cave fossils of *Neocnus comes* reveal that this small Haitian ground sloth faced extinction only 5,000 years ago. It is likely that early humans hunted it for its thick fur.

18. NOTHROTHERIOPS SHASTENSIS

Though medium-sized, *Nothrotheriops shastensis* could really pack a punch. When threatened by predators such as *Smilodon* (p. 76) it could rear up and swipe its large claws in defence.

19. MEGALOCNUS RODENS

Some scientists argue that this sheep-sized ground sloth may have survived in the mountain forests of Cuba until as recently as 400 years ago, around the same time that Europeans first settled in the Americas.

20. THALASSOCNUS CAROLOMARTINI

Thalassocnus carolomartini was one of the last marine sloths. It faced extinction two million years ago, probably as waters cooled due to the connection of North America to South America, which cut off warm ocean currents. Unlike nearly all other sloths, *Thalassocnus carolomartini* had fewer hollow parts in its bones. These incredibly heavy bones helped it to sink to the sea floor to search for food.

FIGURE 1. PILOSA VERTEBRAE

Species of the order Pilosa are most recognisable for having bones in their spine that have extra pointed parts on them, a feature which is unique to mammals. This is a trait Pilosa share with their cousins of a different order, the armadillos (order Cingulata). Together, these two orders are called the Xenarthra (meaning 'strange joints'). Like armadillos, pilosans also have fused bones in their pelvis, most notably the ischium and the sacrum. They also have slower metabolisms than many mammals, which is a feature modern-day tree sloths still have.

Armadillo *vertebrae*

FIGURE 2. BROWN-THROATED SLOTH

The brown-throated sloth *Bradypus variegatus* is the most common three-toed sloth in South America. Its low metabolism and slow-moving character means that it rarely attracts interest from movement-sensitive predators like eagles and other rainforest carnivores. This is an animal that uses its low metabolism to its advantage. Though three-toed sloths look similar to two-toed sloths, the two groups are thought to have split apart from one another more than 40 million years ago. Their similarity is due to convergent evolution, where unrelated animals hit upon the same evolutionary adaptations to fit into a given habitat and end up having similar features in their appearance.

Brown-throated sloth

PROBOSCIDEA

EARLY PALEOGENE TO PRESENT

One could hardly imagine a creature as bizarre as an elephant – a highly intelligent, social creature with an elongated upper lip packed with muscles that allowed it to grasp delicate objects like leaves. But elephants are just one remaining part of a gigantic order that began in Africa and spread throughout the world. On these pages are creatures of this magnificent order, Proboscidea. Early proboscideans were known for their short trunks, and later forms for their pronounced incisors that we call tusks. They include some of the largest mammals that ever walked the Earth, including *Palaeoloxodon namadicus*, which would have rivalled many dinosaurs in shape and size.

1. MAMMUT AMERICANUM

Like modern-day elephants, *Mammut americanum* moved in great herds between feeding grounds. Their favoured habitat was probably spruce woodlands. They had shaggy fur, and their long tusks were straighter than those of most mammoths or elephants.

2. NUMIDOTHERIUM KOHOLENSE

This pint-sized proboscidean stood 1-m-(3-ft)-tall at the shoulder and was more flat-footed than species today. Almost like a tapir, it may have had a muscular upper lip, which it could use to grip and pull leaves and twigs.

Numidotherium koholense

Phosphatherium escuillei

3. PHOSPHATHERIUM ESCUILLEI

Not much bigger than a medium-sized dog, this early proboscidean was a wetland creature that spent much of its time in water. Fossils of its skull show that the jaws were muscular, providing extra power for chewing.

4. DEINOTHERIUM GIGANTEUM

One *Deinotherium giganteum* fossil skull, discovered in 1836, was almost the size of a *Tyrannosaurus rex* skull. It may be that Greek legends of the giant cyclops came from early discoveries of these monstrous skulls.

5. PLATYBELODON GRANGEIR

Some scientists suspect that the sharp edges of *Platybelodon grangeri*'s lower tusks could have been used like a saw. Grasping plants with its muscular trunk, it may have chopped them from branches by pulling them over its lower tusks.

6. ZYGOLOPHODON BORSONI

Zygolophodon borsoni was one of the largest land animals ever. By studying its fossilised teeth and bones, scientists estimate that individual *Zygolophodon borsoni* may have lived for 70 years or more. This is comparable with the lives of elephants today.

7. ELEPHAS CELEBENSIS

This was one of a number of proboscideans that evolved to be a small size by becoming isolated on islands. Dwarf elephants also existed on other islands, including Flores, Indonesia, where a dwarf species of early humans was also known to live.

Elephas celebensis

8. BARYTHERIUM GRAVE

Barytherium grave had four sharp tusks rather than the two tusks that later species had. The upper tusks pointed downwards and the lower tusks pointed forwards. When slotted together, these large tusks may have cut through leaves.

Moeritherium lyonsi

9. MOERITHERIUM LYONSI

The 'beast from Lake Moeris', named after an ancient Egyptian lake, was a 36-million-year-old proboscidean that looked like a tiny hippopotamus. Fossils of its skull suggest it may have had a tapir-like snout that could have helped it pluck the leaves off plants.

10. MAMMUTHUS TROGONTHERII

This 'steppe mammoth' was a Siberian success story. Within thousands of years of its evolution, it had spread throughout much of Europe, including into Britain. Compared to other mammoths, *Mammuthus trogontherii* was huge, perhaps standing as much as 4 m (13 ft) tall at the shoulders.

11. MAMMUTHUS EXILIS

Marooned on the Channel Islands of California, USA, this Columbian mammoth evolved to be a smaller size. Within 20,000 years, what was once a giant proboscidean weighing almost as much as two Indian elephants ended up only weighing as much as a cow.

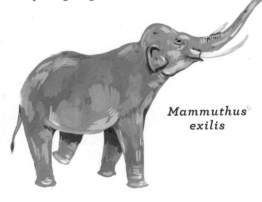

Mammuthus exilis

12. PRODEINOTHERIUM BAVARICUM

Prodeinotherium bavaricum possessed long, downward-pointing incisors on the lower jaw. These might have been used to strip bark from trees. Its short trunk may have grasped leaves, directing mouthfuls of food towards its muscular tongue for chewing.

13. ERITHERIUM AZZOUZORUM

Eritherium azzouzorum showed early signs of having teeth adapted for chewing leaves. Fossils of their jaws show the mammal characteristic of having eight premolars and six molars, a pattern proboscideans would lose as they evolved.

14. MAMMUTHUS CRETICUS

This 'micro-mammoth' once lived in Crete and was about the size of a baby African elephant. Discovered in 2012, fossil bones and teeth findings suggest that it is one of the most fascinating example of island dwarfism known.

Mammuthus creticus

15. PALAEOMASTODON BEADNELLI

Palaeomastodon beadnelli had a long, scoop-shaped lower jaw and a pair of cone-shaped tusks that helped it to pull up swamp plants. Just like modern elephants, *Palaeomastodon beadnelli* had a muscular trunk.

16. AMEBELODON FRICKI

This so-called 'shovel-tusker' was a relative of modern-day elephants that lived in North America six million years ago. Its long, forward-pointing tusks on its lower jaw may have helped it to pull up vegetation or scrape bark from trees.

17. PALAEOLOXODON NAMADICUS

Standing 5 m (16 ft) tall at the shoulders and weighing as much as four Indian elephants, *Palaeoloxodon namadicus* was the largest land animal that has ever lived. Scientists have found evidence of their immense size from a variety of fossil discoveries.

Mammuthus primigenius

18. MAMMUTHUS PRIMIGENIUS

The woolly mammoth is the most well-known extinct proboscidean. Living until 10,000 years ago in Russia, North America and Europe, bodies of woolly mammoths are regularly discovered frozen in ice.

19. DAOUITHERIUM REBOULI

This was one of North Africa's earliest proboscideans. It may have weighed around 180 kg (360 lbs) – about as heavy as a large pig. Although small by today's standards, *Daouitherium rebouli* is thought to have been a giant of the time.

20. ERITREUM MELAKEGHEBREKRISTOSI

This was the first prehistoric proboscidean to have had teeth growing at the back of the jaws that gradually moved forwards to push out the old ones. This growth pattern can be seen in modern-day elephants.

Eritreum melakeghebrekristosi

FIGURE 1. PROBOSCIDIAN TRUNKS

The proboscideans are best known for their multipurpose trunks. Not only can these appendages be used for breathing and showering themselves with water to keep cool, they are also sensitive to touch, and can be used to strip leaves and branches off trees. They are also involved in the production of many of the sounds with which these animals communicate with one another, both now and in the past. Inside the trunk, there are no bones and very little fat. Instead, proboscidean trunks are packed with up to 150,000 muscle fibres, allowing their trunks to move in all directions with ease. Much of the success of the proboscideans is down to this unique adaptation.

1. *Skin*
2. *Muscle fibres*
3. *Nasal passages*

FIGURE 2. AFRICAN BUSH ELEPHANT

Only three species of proboscidean have survived to the modern day, the largest of which is the African bush elephant *Loxodonta africana*. This is the largest and heaviest land animal on Earth, reaching a height of almost 4 m (13 ft) at the shoulders and a weight of more than 10,000 kg (10 t). Elephants are well known for their ability to communicate and their impressive memory. Family groups rely heavily on older females (called matriarchs) to help guide them through hard times such as droughts. Illegal hunting by humans is having a dramatic impact on elephants in the wild. Today, 300,000 bush elephants walk the Earth, but the future of the proboscidean order is far from secure.

African bush elephant

PREHISTORIC CREATURES OF THE ORDER | CARIAMIFORMES

CARIAMIFORMES

EARLY PALEOGENE TO PRESENT

Fossils of these athletic birds are known from all over the world. In South America, Cariformes were at the top of the food chain, rivalling only predatory mammals for the top spot. Among their ranks were the phorusrhacids (known as 'terror birds') and their North American counterparts, the bathornids. Some species weighed almost 500 kg (0.5 t), and at a height of almost 3 m (10 ft) they would have been taller than an Indian elephant. In the last 5 million years many cariamiformes mysteriously disappeared. Today, just two species remain, collectively called the seriemas.

1. PHORUSRHACOS LONGISSIMUS

Phorusrhacos longissimus was the first terror bird discovered. Chancing upon fossils of this unusual creature in 1887, scientists initially believed it was an extinct anteater. A few years later, they realised they had discovered a predatory bird family like no other.

2. PSILOPTERUS BACHMANNI

At 70 cm (27 in) tall, *Psilopterus bachmanni* was one of the smallest terror birds. Like others in its close family, it had sharp, curved claws used for striking prey and possibly also for climbing trees.

Psilopterus bachmanni

3. PATAGORNIS MARSHI

Fossils of its leg bones suggest that *Patagornis marshi* could run 49 km/h (31 mph), about the same speed as an emu or ostrich. These medium-sized terror birds weighed about 25 kg (500 lbs), almost as much as a dalmatian.

4. DEVINCENZIA POZZI

This 2.5-m-(7.8-ft)-tall terror bird ruled South America's grasslands and forests 20 million years ago. Its beak – almost 30 cm (12 in) long – was pointed at the tip. It is named after Garibaldi Devincenzi, a Uruguayan zoologist.

5. LLALLAWAVIS SCAGLIAI

Llallawavis scagliai is known from one of the most complete cariamiform skeletons ever discovered. The fossil, discovered in 2010, shows the bird's entire 1-m-(3-ft)-tall skeleton and even preserved the bones in its eyes and voice box.

6. PROCARIAMA SIMPLEX

Standing 70 cm (27 in) tall, this small terror bird weighed about as much as a dachshund. Its long legs provided speed and agility and its large eyes provided excellent vision to keep watch for predators as well as prey.

Bathornis fax

7. BATHORNIS FAX

It is thought that *Bathornis fax* resembled the only survivor of the cariamiformes today: the seriema. Like the seriema, it probably hunted small prey, such as frogs, lizards and small mammals.

8. BATHORNIS VEREDUS

This emu-sized predator once roamed the central area of North America. *Bathornis* was a rich and diverse family in the cariamiformes order. Five species have been described so far, but there were probably many others.

9. TITANIS WALLERI

Titanis walleri was an agile hunter that may have reached speeds of 100 km/h (62 mph). At 2.5 m (8 ft) tall, it was one of the largest terror birds, though some fossils suggest that males and females differed in size.

Paraphysornis brasiliensis

10. PARAPHYSORNIS BRASILIENSIS

Paraphysornis brasiliensis would have stood as tall as the tallest humans, with a 60-cm-(24-in)-long skull. This is one of the only terror birds known from Brazil, although it is likely that many more fossils await discovery.

11. BATHORNIS GRALLATOR

When first discovered, scientists considered fossils of *Bathornis* to be an unusual form of turkey or vulture. We now know it was a flightless predatory cariamiform, much like the terror birds.

12. PALEOPSILOPTERUS ITABORAIENSIS

This mysterious cariamiform, known only from a handful of fossils found in Brazil in 1985, could have been one of the earliest terror birds. This suggests that terror birds first evolved in South America.

Paleopsilopterus itaboraiensis

13. PARACRAX GIGANTEA

An apex predator, *Paracrax gigantean* hunted alongside hyena-like carnivores and false sabre-toothed cats. Fossils of *Paracrax* were first discovered by a famous fossil hunter from the 1800s, Othniel Charles Marsh. At first, he thought he had found a huge turkey.

14. IDIORNIS TUBERCULATA

Idiornis tuberculata was similar to the seriema, the only cariamiformes alive today. It lived 40 million years ago in what is now Western Europe, hunting small animals. Its long legs might have helped it run away from predators.

Idiornis tuberculata

15. MESEMBRIORNIS INCERTUS

Mesembriornis incertus was perhaps the fastest terror bird ever. Careful study of its fossilised leg bones has suggested that it could run at a staggering 96 km/h (60 mph) – the same speed as a cheetah.

16. BRONTORNIS BURMEISTER

At a height of almost 3 m (10 ft), *Brontornis burmeisteri* would have towered over many predators of the time. Like most predatory dinosaurs, *Brontornis burmeisteri* probably attacked over short distances, relying on ambushing prey at close quarters.

17. ANDALGALORNIS STEULLETI

Armed with a hooked beak almost the size of a brick, *Andalgalornis steulleti* had the largest head for its size of all terror birds. Fossils of its skull and neck suggest its beak could have been used as a weapon.

Strigogyps sapea

18. STRIGOGYPS SAPEA

Strigogyps sapea is perhaps the only herbivore on this page. One skeleton shows fossils of leaves in its stomach area. Its short wings suggest it was flightless, so it probably skulked in the shadows to avoid being eaten.

19. KELENKEN GUILLERMOI

With a skull around 70 cm (26 in) long, *Kelenken guillermoi* is likely to have had the biggest head of any bird ever to have lived. Its 45-cm-(18-ft)-long hooked beak was used as a weapon to immobilise and kill large prey.

20. PSILOPTERUS LEMOINEI

The beaks of *Psilopterus lemoinei* were partly hollow, unlike those of other birds. Rod-like structures throughout the hooked beak gave it strength, helping it to tear apart its prey of lizards and small mammals.

Psilopterus lemoinei

FIGURE 1. LLALLAWAVIS SCAGLIAI

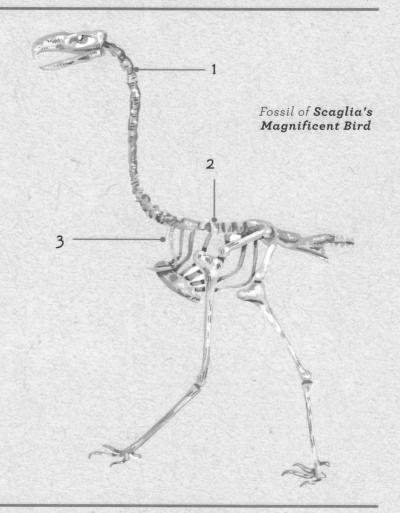

Llallawavis scagliai (Scaglia's Magnificent Bird) is perhaps the best-known fossil skeleton of the phorusrhacids. Discovered by scientists for the first time in 2015, the skeleton includes details of its skull, vertebrae and hips, as well as the bones in the eyes (called sclerotic rings). Unusually, the fossil also shows its complete windpipe.

The upper neck bones of phorusrhacids are more spiny than most flightless birds. This suggests that its neck was highly flexible and well-muscled – designed to help it to strike down on its prey. Its heavy skull and beak may have added momentum for this killer blow.

*Fossil of **Scaglia's Magnificent Bird***

1. *Complete windpipe*
2. *Vertebrae*
3. *Intact ribcage*

FIGURE 2. SERIEMAS

Today, just two cariamiformes remain, and both of these living species resemble the very earliest members of this order known from fossils. They are the red-legged seriema (*Cariama cristata*) and the black-legged seriema (*Chunga burmeisteri*). Both species live in South America. Like many other birds of this order, seriemas are predators that attack and kill small vertebrates including snakes, lizards and frogs, which they pin down with special, sickle-shaped claws and pull apart with sharp beaks. Like most cariamiformes, the seriemas are flightless, although they can flap their wings and take off for short periods when alarmed.

Chunga burmeisteri

Cariama cristata

DIPROTODONTIA

EARLY PALEOGENE TO PRESENT

After it split from Antarctica, 85 million years ago, Australia drifted alone through the ocean, and a unique breed of mammal began to thrive on the continent. These mammals were part of an order called Diprotodontia, which included a host of athletic creatures, including meat-eating kangaroos, and other carnivores in the form of the marsupial lion, an apex predator of its day. But then it all changed. This once-bustling order suffered a sudden wave of extinctions upon the arrival of humans to Australia, 50,000 years ago.

1. PROTEMNODON TUMBUNA

Protemnodon tumbuna may be one of only a handful of kangaroos to have evolved to life on four legs. Fossils show that it used its long, powerful forearms to help with walking, rather like a bandicoot.

2. SILVABESTIUS JOHNILLANDI

A single fossil of a mother and baby is all that is known of this sheep-sized marsupial herbivore. The impressive fossil, unearthed in 1989, shows that when they died, the baby was still inside the mother's pouch.

Silvabestius johnillandi

3. NOTOTHERIUM MITCHELLI

Like horses, *Nototherium,* meaning 'Southern Beast', had teeth that were layered with special enamel that extended beneath the gum line. These so-called 'hypsodont' molars meant that *Nototherium mitchelli*'s teeth didn't suffer much wear throughout life.

4. ZYGOMATURUS TRILOBUS

Built like a hippopotamus, *Zygomaturus trilobus* was likely the largest wetland marsupial. Like hippos, *Zygomaturus trilobus* possessed enormous jaws for chewing wetland plants, and nostrils that were high on the head to help it breathe while submerged.

5. STHENURUS STIRLINGI

These so-called 'strong-tailed' kangaroos were the apex predators of the outback. Sadly, blood-stained tools left behind by early human settlers suggest that *Sthenurus stirlingi* may have been on their menu.

6. WAKALEO SCHOUTENI

Like other marsupial lions, *Wakaleo schouteni* possessed scissor-like premolar teeth used to tear up prey. This species was only named in 2017, after scientists discovered unique fossils of its teeth, skull and forelimb bones.

7. NAMILAMADETA ALBIVENATOR

This mysterious herbivore's name means 'white hunter's changing teeth', which refers to the place where the fossils were discovered – the 'White Hunter Site' in Queensland, Australia – along with the unusual fact that the teeth appear to have been worn down with age.

Procoptodon gilli

8. PROCOPTODON GILLI

By selecting branches and leaves that other kangaroos avoided, *Procoptodon gilliis* managed to survive alongside modern kangaroos until its extinction 50,000 years ago. Early humans may have hunted them, or climate change may have killed off their food.

9. PALORCHESTES AZAEL

Though scientists first thought that this was a kangaroo, *Palorchestes azael* was actually a marsupial herbivore. Fossils of its nose bones suggest that it had a flexible snout, and its unusual jawbone hints at the presence of a giant tongue.

10. ALKWERTATHERIUM WEBBI

About the size of a small bear, this grassland herbivore roamed the wetlands of Australia's northern territory between 12–5 million years ago. *Alkwertatherium webbi* was related to the enormous *Diprotodon*.

11. PROCOPTODON GOLIAH

This giant, short-faced kangaroo stood more than 2 m (7 ft) tall and is likely to have been the biggest kangaroo ever to exist. It had long forearms that were probably used for pulling leaves closer to its mouth.

12. EKALTADETA IMA

This was one of the only known marsupials to have had sharpened molar teeth, used for biting apart insects, and possibly small reptiles and mammals. Though its teeth looked ferocious, *Ekaltadeta ima* was probably an opportunistic omnivore.

Ekaltadeta ima

13. NGAPAKALDIA TEDFORDI

This marsupial moved across the shorelines of lakes within central Australia, 25 million years ago. Its teeth suggest that it was a leaf-eater, possibly feeding upon wetland plants. *Ngapakaldia tedfordi* resembled *Palorchestes*, although it probably lacked the long snout.

14. DIPROTODON OPTATUM

With a body 3 m (10 ft) long and 2 m (7 ft) tall at the shoulders, *Diprotodon optatum* was the largest marsupial ever discovered. Like its surviving cousins, the wombat and the koala, *Diprotodon optatum* had a pouch that pointed backwards.

Hulitherium tomasetti

15. HULITHERIUM TOMASETTI

This bear-like marsupial occupied the dense rainforests of Papua New Guinea until about 10,000 years ago. Standing perhaps 1 m (3 ft) tall, with a body 2 m (7 ft) in length, *Hulitherium tomasetti* may have weighed as much as 200 kg (4,000 lbs).

16. SIMOSTHENURUS OCCIDENTALIS

Simosthenurus occidentalis was about the size of a grey kangaroo, but was far heavier and stockier, perhaps weighing as much as 120 kg (240 lbs). Unlike most kangaroos, this short-faced creature walked rather than hopped.

17. NIMBADON LAVARACKORUM

Nimbadon lavarackorum was the largest tree-living marsupial of its time. Scientists discovered a lot about them in 1990 when they located a hidden Queensland cave within which hundreds of *Nimbadon lavarackorum* fossil bones were found.

Thylacoleo carnifex

18. THYLACOLEO CARNIFEX

This 'predatory pouch lion' was the only marsupial to have retractable claws. These claws were incredibly sharp and may have helped the marsupial climb rock faces to find caves in which they reared their young.

19. MICROLEO ATTENBOROUGHI

Microleo attenboroughi was a pint-size member of the marsupial 'pouch lion' family. Weighing just 600 g (1.3 lbs), its lightweight body allowed it to roam the treetops in search of prey that may have included small mammals, insects and lizards.

Microleo attenboroughi

20. EURYZYGOMA DUNENSE

These giant mammals were unusual for having flared cheekbones that may have been used to store food or, possibly, as a signal to show off their health and prowess to one another.

FIGURE 1. DIPROTODONTIAN FEATURES

One of the secrets behind the success of the order Diprodontia, which includes modern-day kangaroos and wallabies, is their unusual approach to childcare. Females possessed a pouch on their stomachs, inside which their offspring could feed on their milk, and keep safe and warm. This pouch could be used by more than one baby (joey) at a time, with older joeys returning to the pouch to feed alongside their younger siblings. The name 'diprotodont' refers to the pair of large incisors on the lower jaws, which is a feature animals of this order share with the earliest mammals. They also have no canine teeth on the lower jaws. Diprotodonts have unique feet, too. Their second and third toes are fused, though they still have separate claws.

Kangaroo feet

FIGURE 2. RED KANGAROO

The largest surviving member of this order is the red kangaroo *Macropus rufus*, which can reach a standing height of almost 2 m (7 ft.) This is taller than many humans. This herbivore somehow managed to avoid the extinction crisis that devastated the other mammals of its order. It may have survived because it was adaptable to change, but also simply through its speed. In a single leap, the red kangaroo can cover a distance of 8 m (26 ft) or 9 m (29 ft). This jumping style saves them energy, meaning they can achieve a cruising speed far faster than most other land animals.

Red kangaroo

CARNIVORA

EARLY PALEOGENE TO PRESENT

The carnivorans have occupied the top spot in most of the world's ecosystems for many millions of years. Two major groups exist within this order, the cat-like carnivorans (feliforms) and the dog-like carnivorans (caniforms). Both groups have their roots in North America and evolved over 40 million years ago. Like other distinctive mammal groups, this is an order that was once rich in variety, but suffered a number of extinctions, most recently 10,000 years ago. Among prehistoric representatives of this order are the dire wolves, the sabretooths, the cave bears and cheetah-like forms that once raced across the American Plains. There just 280 species of this order alive today.

Simocyon batalleri

1. SIMOCYON BATALLERI

Simocyon batalleriis was thought to be distantly related to the red panda, a bamboo-eating carnivoran that lives in Asia. Fossils of its well-muscled skull and its powerful teeth suggest that it was a carnivore.

2. ICTITHERIUM VIVERRINUM

Packs of these pint-sized predators roamed Eurasia and Africa 7.4 million years ago, probably hunting insects, small mammals and reptiles. How this successful and adaptable hyena species failed to survive into the modern day is a mystery.

Ictitherium viverrinum

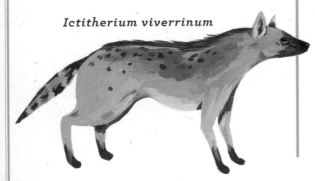

3. PANTHERA LEO SPELAEAN

Found throughout Asia and Europe, this so-called 'cave lion' was often depicted in cave paintings by early humans. Mummified bodies of cave lions have been discovered preserved in ice.

4. BOROPHAGUS DIVERSIDENS

Though dog-like, this so called *Borophagus diversidens* shared many features with hyenas, such as a bulging, muscle-filled skull and powerful jaws armed with crushing premolar teeth used for cracking apart bones.

5. HOPLOPHONEUS OCCIDENTALIS

This large, cat-like creature had giant canine teeth with which it killed its prey. One fossilised skull shows healed bite marks caused by another *Hoplophoneus occidentalis*. This may have been a highly territorial and combative species.

6. IMAGOTARIA DOWNSI

Imagotaria downsi had a number of features that suggest it was an ancestor of the modern-day walrus. Though it lacked the long tusks seen in walrus species today, it possessed enlarged canine tusks and an impressively muscled skull.

Enaliarctos emlongi

7. ENALIARCTOS EMLONGI

Unlike seals that swallow fish whole, it is likely that *Enaliarctos emlongi* had to return to the shoreline to chew fish into smaller chunks using its sharp molars.

8. BARBOUROFELIS LOVEORUM

This sabretooth-like family of predators evolved in Africa 20 million years ago and, after many millions of years, moved through Europe and Asia before colonising North America via an ice-covered land bridge.

Barbourofelis loveorum

9. ARCTOTHERIUM BONARIENSE

Arctotherium bonariense could stand 3 m (10 ft) tall, making it possibly the largest bear ever to have walked the Earth. *Arctotherium bonariense* is one of the South American short-faced bears that thrived 1.2 million years ago, before becoming mysteriously extinct.

10. CHAMITATAXUS AVITUS

This early badger roamed North America about 6 million years ago. Like modern-day badgers, its strong jaws could kill small creatures with a single bite. The ear-holes in its skull suggest it could hear low-frequency sounds over long distances.

Chamitataxus avitus

11. AMPHICYON INGENS

This was one of the largest of the so-called 'bear-dogs' that lived across North America 15 million years ago. Weighing more than 600 kg (1,300 lbs), it was more than twice as heavy as a lion, and far stockier.

12. PARAMACHAIRODUS ORIENTALIS

Paramachairodus orientalis was an impressive climber. Its flexible hind limbs suggest that it was better at climbing trees than today's leopards. Many fossils have been found in Spain's Cerro de los Batallones, a site famous for its fossils of carnivores.

Paramachairodus orientalis

Dinocrocuta gigantea

13. DINOCROCUTA GIGANTEA

Scientists are unsure whether this hyena-like predator was a solitary hunter or whether it hunted in packs. A fossilised rhinoceros skull bearing bite marks from *Dinocrocuta gigantea* suggests that it hunted prey much bigger than itself.

14. HEMICYON SANSANIENSIS

This stocky, 1.5 m-(4.9-ft)-long carnivoran was built for long-distance running. Its long, athletic toes resembled those of a wolf and it may have chased animals over hundreds of metres, waiting for its prey to tire.

15. MIRACINONYX INEXPECTATUS

Though it was probably unrelated to modern-day cheetahs, this large and slender cat evolved many of the same adaptations for speed, including a light skeleton, a short skull with wide nostrils and a long tail.

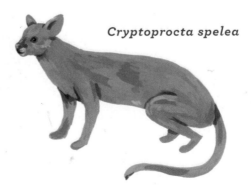

Cryptoprocta spelea

16. CRYPTOPROCTA SPELEA

Cryptoprocta spelea was a giant relative of the modern fossa, and likely faced extinction in the last 1,000 years or so. Some scientists believe that this giant fossa might still live today in remote parts of Madagascar.

17. HOMOTHERIUM LATIDENS

Although *Homotherium latidens'* blade-like canines were smaller than those of the sabretoothed cats, its powerful jaws could be used for gripping and pulling apart prey.

18. URSUS SPELAEUS

Like the brown bear, *Ursus spelaeus* was an omnivore. In fact, evidence from its teeth suggests that it may have been more herbivorous than other bears. A century ago, scientists exploring a cave in Switzerland unearthed more than 30,000 fossil skeletons.

Canis dirus

19. CANIS DIRUS

This monstrous pack hunter was similar in size to modern-day wolves, but its canine bite strength was more powerful than any known wolf species. This so-called 'dire wolf' preyed upon horses, ground sloths, camels, bison and mastodons.

20. SMILODON POPULATOR

Armed with killer canines almost 30 cm (12 in) long, and a jaw capable of opening twice as wide as modern-day lions, this huge sabretooth was undoubtedly the most feared predator of the Americas.

Smilodon populator

FIGURE 1. CARNIVORAN TEETH

Carnivorans are known for their distinctive teeth. Many species possess large canines used for pulling apart bones and tough incisors for stripping meat, but most unusual are their molar teeth. All carnivorans possess an extra-sharp enlarged upper molar and lower pre-molar tooth that cut across one another when the jaws snap shut. Carnivorans use these cutting blades to shear through the bones and cartilage of prey. These so-called 'carnassial teeth' are an important adaptation for carnivorans and are one reason for their global domination.

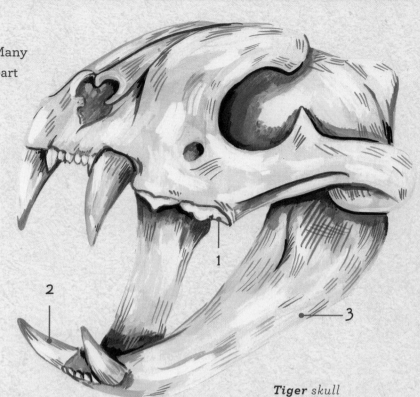

1. *Upper molar*
2. *Canine*
3. *Jaw bone*

Tiger *skull*

FIGURE 2. TIGER

The tiger is a big cat with history on its side. Fossils of tigers are known from the island of Java and have been dated to 1.7 million years old, meaning that they lived alongside many of the other carnivorans on these pages. Fossil finds clearly show the spread of the tiger across the Asian continent, moving through Sumatra and China one million years ago and ending up in Japan in the last 100,000 years. Sadly, the tiger's impressive knack for colonising new continental regions did not continue. In the last 1,000 years, humans armed with weapons have pushed them back across Asia, killing them in their thousands to protect themselves and their livestock. The downward trend continues to this day, with only a few thousand tigers still remaining in the wild.

Sumatran tiger

GLOSSARY

ADAPTATION

The way an organism changes to be better at surviving and thriving in its environment.

APEX PREDATOR

An animal at the top of the food chain, which is not hunted by any other creatures.

BENTHIC

The lowest level of a body of water.

BILL

Another name for a bird's beak.

CAMOUFLAGE

The way an animal may disguise itself against its environment as a defence against predators.

CARNIVORE

An animal that eats meat.

CONVERGENT EVOLUTION

When separate organisms evolve in similar ways to suit their environment.

CRUSTACEAN

A shelled, underwater arthropod.

DISPLAY

The way animals behave to convey information to other animals, sometimes in the same species, sometimes a different one.

DRAG

When air or water pulls on a moving object to slow it down.

ECOSYSTEM

An environment and the organisms that live in it.

EMBRYO

An animal in the first stages of its development, usually still within the egg or uterus.

EVOLUTION

The process by which living things change over time.

EXTINCT

A species that has died out and has no living members.

FOSSIL

The remains of a dead plant of animal preserved in rock.

GILLS

Flaps at the side of fish and some amphibians' heads, which allow them to breathe underwater.

GLAND

An organ that creates chemicals for the body to use.

HERBIVORE

An animal that eats plants.

INCISORS

The serrated teeth at the front of an animal's mouth

INVERTEBRATE

Creatures that do not have a backbone.

JUVENILE

The animal life-stage before adulthood.

LARVAE

A young insect, in the stage between egg and pupa.

LATERAL LINE

Sensory organs that allow aquatic creatures, including some fish and amphibians, to sense movement underwater.

MAMMALS

A group of warm-blooded, often hairy animals that give milk to their young.

MATING

When two animals come together to breed.

MATRIARCH

A female who is the head of a family or group.

METABOLISM

The processes that occur within a living creature that allows it to maintain life.

METAMORPHOSIS

A change from one form to another in the life of an animal, like the change from caterpillar to butterfly.

MOMENTUM

The power created by moving.

OFFSPRING

The children, or young, of a specific species.

OPPORTUNISTIC

An organism that is able to spread quickly in an unexplored habitat.

ORGANISM

A living thing, a specific animal, plant, fungus, or bacteria.

PANORAMIC

A 360 degree view.

PARALLEL

Running alongside something else.

PECTORAL FIN

The fins on either side of a sea creature's head.

PERISCOPE

A type of telescope, often used on submarines, to allow someone to see things that are out of sight.

PREDATOR

An animal that hunts other animals for food.

PREY

An animal that is fed on by other animals.

PRIMITIVE

Simple, not highly evolved.

SCAVENGER

A creature that feeds on dead animals.

SEDIMENT

The material at the bottom of a river, lake, pond or ocean.

SPECIES

A particular type of plant, animal or living thing.

SUBTERRANEAN

Being, living or operating under the earth.

TAXONOMY

The branch of science that classifies living things.

TERRESTRIAL

A creature that lives on dry land.

TUBERCLE

A small, rounded part of a bone that sticks out.

TYMPANUM

A thin membrane over an ear or hearing organ.

VERTEBRATE

A creature with a central nerve cord, often with a backbone.

CREDITS

ILLUSTRATED BY KELSEY OSEID
WRITTEN BY JULES HOWARD

Kelsey Oseid is an illustrator, author, and amateur naturalist. Her gauche illustrations focus on natural history subjects like taxonomy, biodiversity, and taxidermy, as well as related subjects like astronomy and the ways humans relate to the natural world.

Jules Howard is a zoologist, non-fiction author, and international ambassador for science. As well as writing regularly for The Guardian and the BBC, Jules offers support to a number of non-fiction book publishers working on zoological themes, including Templar and Bloomsbury.

Ichthyosaurus communis, Brachypterygius extremus, Temnodontosaurus platyodon, Dearcmhara shawcrossi, Excalibosaurus costini, Wahlisaurus massarae